D0216129

THE COMMONWEALTH AND INTERNATIONAL LIBRARY
Joint Chairmen of the Honorary Editorial Advisory Board
SIR ROBERT ROBINSON, O. M., F.R.S., LONDON
DEAN ATHELSTAN SPILHAUS, MINNESOTA

SELECTED READINGS IN PHYSICS
General Editor: D. TER HAAR

MEN OF PHYSICS

JULIUS ROBERT MAYER

Prophet of Energy

MEN OF PHYSICS

JULIUS ROBERT MAYER
Prophet of Energy

BY

ROBERT BRUCE LINDSAY

Emeritus Professor of Physics, Brown University

PERGAMON PRESS

Oxford · New York · Toronto
Sydney · Braunschweig

QC16
M47L56

PERGAMON PRESS LTD.
Headington Hill Hall, Oxford

PERGAMON PRESS INC.
Maxwell House, Fairview Park, Elmsford, New York 10523

PERGAMON OF CANADA LTD.
207 Queen's Quay West, Toronto 1

PERGAMON PRESS (AUST.) PTY. LTD.
19a Boundary Street, Rushcutters Bay, N.S.W. 2011, Australia

VIEWEG & SOHN GmbH
Burgplatz 1, Braunschweig

Copyright © 1973 Pergamon Press Ltd.

*All Rights Reserved. No part of this publication may be reproduced,
stored in a retrieval system, or transmitted, in any form nor by any means,
electronic, mechanical, photocopying, recording or otherwise, without
the prior permission of Pergamon Press Limited*

First edition 1973

Library of Congress Cataloging in Publication Data

Lindsay, Robert Bruce, 1900–
  Men of physics.

  (The Commonwealth and international library.
Selected readings in physics)
    Bibliography: p.
    1. Mayer, Julius Robert von, 1814–1878. I. Title.
QC16.M47L56   536'.7'0924 [B]   72–8045
ISBN 0-08-016985-6

Printed in Hungary

Contents

CONTENTS

PART III

ON THE QUANTITATIVE AND QUALITATIVE DETERMINATION OF FORCES

ON THE FORCES OF INORGANIC NATURE

THE MOTIONS OF ORGANISMS AND THEIR RELATION TO METABOLISM. AN ESSAY IN NATURAL SCIENCE

CELESTIAL DYNAMICS

COMMENTS ON THE MECHANICAL EQUIVALENT OF HEAT

PREFACE

THE name of Julius Robert Mayer is not as well known as it ought to be among scientists and philosophers in English-speaking countries. The first person to emphasize the importance of the concept of energy in science as a whole and the first to calculate theoretically the mechanical equivalent of heat, he was one of the founders of thermodynamics and biophysics. As an amateur in science, the story of his accomplishments and his fate in life should be of significance to all who are in any way interested in the history of science.

The purpose of this volume is to provide an appraisal of Mayer's scientific work together with translations of all his important papers on the concept of energy. Except where otherwise noted, the translations are those of the author of this book. Frequent editorial notes serve to clarify points in Mayer's writings which may be obscure to the modern reader.

The book is introduced by a brief biographical sketch, which necessarily leans heavily on the German works mentioned in the Bibliography at the end of the volume. Part II is a critical evaluation of Mayer's scientific accomplishments, involving an analysis of the various articles. Part III consists of the text of Mayer's five articles on the concept of energy, arranged in chronological order.

It is a pleasure to acknowledge the encouragement received from Dr. D. ter Haar, the general editor of the series. Grateful acknowledgement is also due to the various German sources for details about Mayer's life and work, particularly the volume by Schmolz and Weckbach mentioned in the Bibliography. The author is grateful for the privilege of an interview with Mr. Weckbach in which material in the archives of the city of Heilbronn relating to Mayer was made available for his inspection. The author is particularly appreciative of the help rendered by Miss Susan Desilets of the Department of Physics in Brown University in connection with the typing of the manuscript.

Providence, Rhode Island   R. B. L.

PART I

Biographical Sketch

THE subject of this sketch was an interesting example of the role of the gifted amateur in the evolution of scientific concepts. Trained as a physician and spending the larger part of his life as a practitioner of medicine in the town of Heilbronn in Würtemberg in southern Germany, he yet was consumed with the idea of generalizing the idea of energy to all human experience and became a principal founder of thermodynamics. His story is the story of a genius in the relentless pursuit of a single idea, but it is also a tale of frustration and tragedy which has few parallels in the history of science.

Julius Robert Mayer was a Swabian born on November 25, 1814 in the city of Heilbronn in what is now the German state of Baden-Würtemberg. Now a bustling industrial city of some 50,000 people lying on the Neckar between Stuttgart and Heidelberg, in Mayer's childhood it was a quiet country town with roots going back to the eighth century when it was part of the Frankish crown-lands.

Mayer's forbears were of Swabian descent on both sides. His father ran an apothecary shop in Heilbronn and was much interested in chemistry and scientific experiments in general. He lived to the age of 82. His mother (maiden name Heermann) was less healthy and is said to have developed some eccentricities though no serious mental disorders. Mayer's older brother went into the father's business. It seems that Robert was intended for medicine from the outset. He attended the local schools and in particular the Gymnasium in Heilbronn, where he was exposed to the classical curriculum prevailing at that time. It is reported that he developed an antipathy to the classical languages, though he did well in mathematics. School work in science was minimal, but Mayer picked up some acquaintance with physics, chemistry and biology through experiments performed at home with the help of his brother.

3

At the age of 15 Mayer left the Gymnasium and took up residence in a seminary in nearby Schöntal to prepare for entrance to the university. Here he was referred to by his friends as "Geist" because of his ability to perform clever scientific tricks. His actual academic work was on the whole rather mediocre, though he did well in history. He seems to have been of an independent turn of mind and not very docile under discipline. He developed a liking for poetry and novels and became particularly fond of Sir Walter Scott's works. There is no record of any interest in art or music.

In 1832 Mayer matriculated at the University of Tübingen for the study of medicine. Here it does not appear that he was a very zealous student, save in anatomy, a course he took six times. He studied no mathematics or philosophy and had only one semester of physics under a *privat dozent*. Much time was spent on extra-curricular activities, including his fraternity. Mayer evidently was popular with his fellow students and became an expert card and billiard player. He eventually got into trouble with the university authorities in connection with his membership in a forbidden organization. In fact in 1837 after five years of residence he was suspended for a period of one year and had to leave Tübingen. This suspension was taken very hard and Mayer went on a six-day hunger strike. The physician who examined Mayer on this occasion reported that the mental condition of the student might be seriously affected if he were thwarted in his desires. It is difficult to assess the significance of this incident, since it is well known that young people considered perfectly normal do occasionally manage to do strange things. However, some might see in this a premonition of Mayer's later mental difficulties.

After short visits to Munich and Vienna where there is little indication of any particular accomplishment, Mayer was permitted to return to Tübingen in January 1838. He then finished his dissertation, passed his doctoral examination and received his M.D. degree. His dissertation was a rather routine clinical study of the drug santonin, a remedy for intestinal worms. It gave no hint of his future scientific competence.

At this stage, Mayer came to a decision reflecting an independence of judgment and spirit which one must admit did decidedly fore-shadow his future independence of mind. Instead of settling down to a routine practice of medicine in his native city as his relatives expected he would do, he decided to travel and in particular to see a quite different part of the world. Much against parental advice he determined to ship as a doctor on board a Dutch vessel trading with the East Indies. This meant securing a medical license from the Netherlands. He passed this examination with nothing better than a "satisfactory" rating in the summer of 1839 and then spent six months in Paris while waiting for his ship to sail. Evidently this time was largely devoted to observing French medical practices. There is no evidence that he endeavored to improve his grasp of physics, chemistry and mathema-tics, in spite of the fact that he enjoyed in Paris the company of his young compatriot Carl Baur, who later became Professor of Mathe-matics in Stuttgart and in later years helped Mayer considerably with his mathematical difficulties.

On February 22, 1840 Mayer embarked from Rotterdam on the sailing ship *Java* bound for Batavia. The voyage took three months, and though a diary was kept, not a great deal of interest can be gleaned from it, except that the ship's doctor did not have much work to do, had little association with the ship's officers, felt he often did not get enough to eat and spent a large fraction of his time reading scientific books he had brought with him. There seems, however, to have been nothing in this reading to prepare him for the discovery he made shortly after arrival in the roadstead of Surabaya in East Java, when he had occasion to let blood from some of the sailors on the ship. He was surprised to find the venous blood a much brighter red than expected, and at first thought he had struck an artery. Discussion with physicians in the East Indies, however, verified that this was a common observation in the Tropics. This observation, taking place around the middle of July 1840, was the spark that set off the whole train of Mayer's thought culminating in the generalization of the con-cept of energy. The redness of the venous blood means less oxidation of the food consumed and hence less heat produced. The person living in the Tropics does not need this heat and hence will not oxidize as much food material. This stimulated a train of thought in Mayer, in which the work done by bodily exertion also entered. The substance of his speculation is set forth in greater detail in Part II, where Mayer's scientific achievements are analyzed. It is sufficient to point out here that once Mayer had become excited with this biophysical puzzle he was obsessed by it and its scientific consequences for the rest of his professional career. He later said that he was so impressed with the possible importance of the idea which came to him as a result of the simple blood-letting observation that he spent most of the time while his ship was in Java on board meditating on it and rarely went ashore for exploration. The ship sailed back to the Netherlands late in September 1840 and Mayer was back in Heilbronn again in February 1841.

Mayer immediately began the practice of medicine in Heilbronn and must have been considered an effective physician, for in addition to acquiring an extensive private practice he was after a short time appointed chief town surgeon. But he almost at once began to review and renew his scientific speculations. He convinced himself that there must be a constant relation between heat and work. Unfortunately his ideas about physics were very fuzzy. He tended to think along philosophical lines and these seemed to possess an air of plausibility. But to get anything that would appeal to physicists he had to bring in some concrete physics and here he was at first woefully weak.

Mayer put together his ideas in the form of a paper with the German title "Über die quantitative and qualitative Bestimmung der Kräfte". This we may translate as "On the quantitative and qualitative determination of forms of energy". It must be remembered that the German word *Kraft* and the corresponding English word "force" were used at the time Mayer wrote not in the precise technical sense in which they are used in mechanics today, but in a sense to which we now give the name energy. This paper was submitted in June 1841 to Poggendorf's *Annalen der Physik und Chemie*. It was not accepted for publication, nor was it ever returned with any explanation of its fate. The physics in it was based on a profound misunderstanding of mechanics and it was a good thing for Mayer's subsequent reputation that it did not then see the light of day. An English translation of the article is presented in Part III of this book; a critique is given in Part II.

In a certain sense this marks the beginnings of Mayer's troubles—the tacit rejection of his ideas. He obviously at this time did not know enough fundamental science to present his view in logical fashion. Fortunately he was not discouraged. He had correspondence with his friend Baur, at that time in Tübingen, and also the professor of physics at Tübingen, Nörremberg. At any rate by September, 1841 he was able to get his ideas straightened out sufficiently to carry through a calculation of the mechanical equivalent of heat based on the thermal properties of gases. A short paper containing his result, though without the actual computational details, was submitted to Liebig's *Annalen der Chemie und Pharmacie* in March 1842 and was published before the end of the year [vol. 42, p. 233, 1842]. A critique of this basic paper will be found in Part II of this book and an English translation is given in Part III. The paper received little or no attention; at any rate from those competent to judge its importance. The choice of a journal of chemistry and pharmacology was undoubtedly unfortunate. The results apparently failed to come to the attention of people like Joule and Colding, who were concerning themselves with similar ideas, though from a different standpoint. Mayer's friends in the vicinity of Heilbronn, who sympathized with him and tried to encourage him, were not scientists of any great weight or influence.

Mayer was still young and buoyant enough to feel that recognition would come. The next few years were generally happy ones. The year 1842 saw his marriage to Wilhelmine Closs of Winnenden, and he seemed to be settling down to a pleasant domestic existence with a profitable medical practice and a recognized professional position in the community. It might indeed have been better for his own peace of mind and his domestic happiness if he had been content with this sort of existence. But he was driven by a consuming desire to erect his view of the relation between heat and work into an all-embracing scientific theory. As he wrote to his friend Griesinger in December 1842: "It is my assertion that motion, heat, light, electricity and the various chemical reactions are all one and the same object under differently appearing forms."

The years from 1843 to 1845 were taken up with the preparation of his second article. Here he evidently profited greatly by the presence in Heilbronn of friend Baur, who gave him lessons in mathematics and mechanics and who read and criticized various parts of his new work. Baur, in particular, urged him to amplify his presentation so as to make his ideas clearer and hopefully thereby gain a larger audience than he had been able to reach by his relatively short 1842 paper. Mayer proceeded to take this advice and also decided to show how his fundamental conceptions could be applied to physiology. So his new paper bore the German title: "Die organische Bewegung in ihrem Zusammenhang mit dem Stoffwechsel. Ein Beitrag zur Naturkunde" ("Motion in organisms and its connection with metabolism. A contribution to natural science"). It was an unfortunate title, for it did not really provide a clear idea of the contents, as will become apparent from the translation of the paper in Part III of this book and the critical commentary in Part II. At any rate the paper was submitted to Liebig's *Annalen*, but was declined. Liebig's assistant gave as the reason the fact that the journal was at the time overstocked with chemical papers. Evidently he had not taken the trouble to read it with any care. Poggendorf was recommended as an alternative, but Mayer had no stomach for this after his first experience. Moreover, it seems almost certain that the paper would have been rejected had it been submitted. The essay was finally printed privately at Mayer's expense by the Drechsler Bookstore in Heilbronn in the year 1845. It was a long article, almost semi-book length with 112 pages. In many ways this was the most important of Mayer's papers. Detailed comment on it is deferred to Part II of this book.

There is no record of the circulation Mayer provided for his 1845 essay. Presumably he sent it to well-known physicists and biologists and certainly to learned journals for review. However, beyond a few rather perfunctory notices in the periodicals, it got little or no attention. This neglect was taken rather hard by Mayer, but he still persisted in following up his ideas and in 1848 brought out another long essay with the German title: "Beiträge zur Dynamik des Himmels in populärer Darstellung" ("Contributions to Celestial Mechanics, popularly presented"). This again was privately printed in Heilbronn. In this article Mayer endeavored to account for the heat of the sun from the transformation into heat of the mechanical energy of meteorites falling into the sun, an idea revived (with no reference to Mayer, however) by Lord Kelvin some years later. The essay is presented in full in Part III and a critique is given in Part II. Misfortune dogged Mayer again. The year 1848 was a bad time in bring out a scientific paper, since this was the time of revolutionary activity in Germany and indeed other parts of Europe as well: Mayer even had family problems connected with this movement, since his older brother joined the revolutionaries. This caused Mayer much expense and embarrassment.

It was also in 1846 and 1848, respectively, that three of Mayer's children died, causing much personal grief. There is some evidence that his domestic life was not entirely happy. His preoccupation with his scientific investigations along with his medical practice may well have made him a somewhat difficult person to get along with, even though his general disposition is said to have been good. Moreover, he had begun to take rather seriously the lack of recognition for what he thought he had accomplished. In the meantime Mayer's work had come to the attention of J. P. Joule in England, who in 1843 had published his first estimate of the mechanical equivalent as determined from his experimental measurements. Joule ultimately published in 1847 in the *Comptes Rendues* of the Academy of Sciences in Paris an account of his own work and a reference to that of Mayer in which he claimed that Mayer's theoretical derivation of the mechanical equivalent of heat was based on a fundamental assumption which was totally unjustified at the time Mayer used it and was only made reasonable by later experiments by Joule himself. This stimulated Mayer to reply that the experiment in question (on the free expansion of gases) had been done long before Joule by the Frenchman Gay-Lussac and provided the basis of his (Mayer's) calculation. This silenced Joule for the time being, but hardly helped Mayer, for he was presently attacked in his own country by a young *privat-dozent* named Seyffer, who published in a newspaper an article practically claiming that Mayer was an ignoramus and the mechanical theory of heat was a joke. Unfortunately Mayer took this ridiculous affair seriously and went to the trouble of making a public answer. All this served to upset his somewhat excitable temperament and undoubtedly assisted in bringing about his nervous breakdown.

Matters came to a crisis in May 1850. During an attack of insomnia Mayer jumped from his bedroom window to the street below, a fall of nine meters. He luckily escaped without serious internal injuries or major fracture of bones but he did damage his feet severely and took a long time to recuperate. For a time his medical practice suffered and he seems to have turned to religious mysticism to try to regain his composure. He evidently realized he needed some help, but was uncertain where to turn for it. His mental situation grew worse in the fall of 1851 and he decided voluntarily to enter a private sanatorium operated by a Dr. Laderer in the town of Göppingen, some 25 miles southeast of Stuttgart. The treatment here was not successful and he had to be removed to the state asylum in the same town under the direction of Dr. Zeller. It is generally agreed that he was here treated very badly, even confined for a time in a straightjacket. He was released from this institution in September 1853. According to one source, the hospital authorities felt his case was hopeless and he was not likely to live much longer in any case. His scientific preoccupations seem to have been much on his mind during this whole ordeal and must have complicated treatment.

The whole story of Mayer's illness is a very complicated one. It apparently aroused considerable interest in medical circles after Mayer's death, and a good deal of material on it was published, much of it taking the attitude that Mayer was ill used. Evidence exists that Mayer in later life was never willing to admit that he was insane at any time. There seems little doubt, however, that he exhibited schizophrenic behavior at various intervals over a good many years. After his confinement and release, when he returned to Heilbronn and after a time resumed a limited medical practice, he disappeared effectively from the scientific scene for a matter of ten years. The ideas he had developed were extended to form the foundations of thermodynamics by scientists like Clausius, Helmholtz, Kelvin and Rankine. Much of what Mayer had done was independently rediscovered by these professionals in the field, and his early contributions were largely forgotten. Even those who were fully aware of the magnitude of his achievement thought he was no longer alive. When Liebig, in a lecture in Munich in 1858, paid tribute to Mayer he announced to the audience that unfortunately Mayer had died a premature death in an insane asylum. This statement was printed in the report of Liebig's lecture. The report was naturally denied from Heilbronn, but the denial went unnoticed, and Mayer's "death" was officially recorded in Poggendorf's *Handwörterbuch*. A correction was inserted later in the supplement, but few people consult supplements. To all intents and purposes Mayer was effectively "dead" so far as the scientific public was concerned.

In the meantime Mayer lived quietly with gradually returning health. Occasionally, however, the thought of his failure to secure the recognition he deserved would bring on a bad spell. It was not until 1862 he emerged from scientific obscurity to write a paper "On Fever" for the *Arkiv der Heilkunde*. This was not a work of much originality, but rather a summary of well-known facts on the subject.

Somewhat earlier Mayer began to receive the tardy recognition of his scientific achievements. In 1858 he was made an honorary member of the Basel Academy of Natural Sciences, largely through the efforts of the chemist Schönbein. Around 1860 he began to attend scientific meetings and gave numerous general addresses. It does not appear that these materially enhanced his reputation. He found it difficult to keep his fundamentalist religious views out of his remarks, and this did not go down well with the scientists of that time. He was definitely antagonistic to the Darwinism theory of evolution and even in his own special field of energy transformations was unsympathetic with developments connected with the second law of thermodynamics.

The first open recognition by a physicist of international reputation of Mayer's claim to priority in connection with heat and work came interestingly enough from the Englishman John Tyndall, professor at the Royal Institution of Great Britain. At an international scientific meeting in London in 1862 Tyndall gave a lecture in which he reviewed the development of the mechanical theory of heat. He took occasion to give Mayer full credit for his pioneering work. Though by no means adulatory, the remarks were sufficiently emphatic with respect to Mayer's priority as to arouse resentment in British scientific circles. Joule was stimulated to write a polite but questioning letter to the *Philosophical Magazine*, to which Tyndall replied by publishing in the same journal translations of Mayer's 1842 and 1848 papers as a support for the assertions in his lecture. This led to a rather acrimonious controversy between Tyndall and P. G. Tait of the University of Edinburgh, who seemed unwilling to accept Mayer's claims as really worthy of scientific credence. Lord Kelvin (then still Sir William Thomson) was drawn into the controversy, partly in view of his own contributions to the newly founded theory of thermodynamics and partly in support of his close friend and colleague Tait. His comments were on a somewhat more lofty tone, though it must have rankled a bit to have Tyndall call attention to Mayer's anticipation of his (Kelvin's) meteoric theory of the origin of the sun's heat. Tyndall again reviewed Mayer's work at some length in his book *Heat As a Mode of Motion* (London, 1863). The story is not a very happy one and it seems unfortunate that Tyndall's championing of an amateur like Mayer should have led to such deterioration of personal relations. It appears that Tyndall had the better of the argument. At all events, Mayer was awarded the Copley medal of the Royal Society of London in 1871, one year after it was presented to Joule.

It was apparently suggested to Mayer in the late 1860s that he should write a physical textbook or treatise on heat embodying the new thermodynamic ideas. This he said he could not do. However, in 1869 there was brought out by Cotta in Stuttgart a collected edition of Mayer's writings. This was reissued in revised and enlarged form in 1893 under the editorship of Jacob J. Weyrauch, who also included in it a collection of Mayer's correspondence.

In 1873 there appeared Eugen Dühring's critical history of the principles of mechanics. In the biographical dictionaries Dühring is listed as a philosopher and political economist. However, he took a deep interest in the philosophy of science and was a prolific writer. In his book he advanced strong claims for Mayer's priority in establishing the mechanical theory of heat and the generalized concept of energy. His rather harsh criticism of other workers in the field led to a controversy with Hermann von Helmholtz, which ultimately caused Dühring's withdrawal from his teaching position at the University of Berlin. Dühring was evidently a man who could develop very strong feelings on any subject both pro and con and did not hesitate to express them freely in exaggerated terms. His attacks on the university "establishment" in Berlin were virulent and evidently produced a sensation at the time. It should be emphasized that poor Mayer was innocent in all this. He apparently did read Dühring's book, but either from modesty or otherwise refrained from writing to the author. Finally Dühring sent to Mayer some reviews of his book with presumably some account of the row in Berlin circles. Mayer then (June 22, 1877) wrote to Dühring to express his concern that Dühring should have suffered so much trouble for his (Mayer's) sake.

Mayer and Dühring finally met late in July 1877 in the vacation town of Wildbad, where Dühring and his family were vacationing. Some may think it curious that Mayer did not invite him to Heilbronn. At any rate Dühring tells the story of his conversations with Mayer in his book *Robert Mayer—der Galileo des neunzehnten Jahrhunderts*, published by Verlag Ernst Schmetzer in Chemnitz, 1880, after Mayer's death. In the interview Mayer appeared more willing to talk about his health problems than about conservation of energy. In particular he insisted that he had never been insane and that he had suffered dreadful treatment while in the asylum in Winnental. All this is set forth in rather exaggerated detail in Dühring's book, along with his view that Mayer had been deliberately persecuted by the "guild of professionals" in Germany. It is difficult to believe all this, motivated as it doubtless was by Dühring's great dislike of Helmholtz. During his active scientific career Mayer could not avoid being considered an amateur by the professionals even though he did not want to be so considered. The way of an amateur among professionals has always been hard.

Dühring is also responsible for the allegation that Mayer's domestic life was not too happy. Mrs. Mayer is said to have been a strong-minded masculine type of woman, and it may have been too much to expect that she would sympathize greatly with her husband's scientific efforts, particularly as they seemed to interfere with his economic situation. Her relatives probably felt even more strongly the folly of Mayer's amateur efforts, particularly since they did not bring any obvious fame for such a long time and then only after the long, hard ordeal of mental illness. Dühring would even have us believe that Mrs. Mayer's relatives made little effort to secure Mayer's release from the mental institution and actually elaborated the story of his insanity. On the other hand, the letters of Mayer included in the collected works as published by Weyrauch contain nothing on which Düring's judgment could be legitimately based. It has been pointed out by Ostwald, however, that the letters in question were handed over to Weyrauch after Mayer's death by his relatives. One might have one's suspicions raised by this. It is doubtless best to draw a veil over these considerations, especially in the light of the fact that by his very temperament Mayer was undoubtedly a somewhat difficult man to live with, particularly in his excited and bitter moods.

In 1876, two years before his death, Mayer brought out his last scientific paper. Entitled "Auslösung", it dealt with phenomena in which a small amount of energy can control the release of a relatively large amount as in an explosion or a chain reaction generally. Mayer was here interested primarily in physiological illustrations. In particular he paid a lot of attention to neurological processes, using his own nervous breakdown as an example. The obsession with his own health problem at his age may be considered significant. The article probably should not be considered of any great scientific significance.

Mayer was apparently destined to be dogged by external impacts which produced bitterness even in his declining years, when one might have supposed he would mellow with the final recognition in the form of honorary memberships in learned societies and an honorary degree. However, this was not the case.

Mayer's sensitive nature was upset by what he considered to be a scarcely veiled slur on his scientific achievements by Helmholtz. In an address in 1877 before a scientific audience entitled "Über das Denken in der Medizin" (On Thought in Medicine), Helmholtz introduced the following observation:

"It is easy to find superficial analogies which are entertaining in lay circles, and the turning up of clever coincidences soon confers on their author the reputation of being an ingenious person. Among a large number of such coincidental ideas there are bound to be some which turn out to be correct at least in part, possibly in whole. It would indeed be too clever by far to be always wrong! In the case of the lucky ideas, one can make good a claim to priority of the discovery; if it does not lead to success, a happy forgetfulness will damp out all memory of failure. . . . A scientific investigator who does not choose to bring his ideas to market until he has verified them from every possible angle, has removed all objection and has firmly established his demonstration, suffers thereby an unmistakable disadvantage. The prevailing system of deciding priority questions only through the date of the first publication without taking into consideration the maturity of the work, materially favors this disorderly situation."

To most people, scientists and lay persons alike, these observations of Helmholtz seem eminently reasonable, if taken in a general context. Mayer, however, seems to have taken it for granted that they were directed at him. On the face of it this was not a very rational attitude in the light of Helmholtz's previous public recognition and praise of Mayer's work. Though there may have been some justification for Mayer's attitude that the record does not directly reveal, it would appear that he was somewhat too ready to take offense where none may have been intended. He found it hard to endure even an implied slight. It would probably have been better all round had he not prepared a review of Helmholtz's lecture in which he quoted Arago's definition of what constitutes priority in scientific discovery, namely the date of publication of the first reference to it. This was fair enough, but Mayer did not stop there: he went on to assume that Helmholtz had him in mind and then proceeded to defend his (Mayer's) claim once more to priority in the mechanical theory of heat controversy. He certainly had a right to assert his own "maturity" in the light of his 1845 and 1848 papers. But it all seemed so unnecessary as the somewhat childish resentment of a bitter old man.

The problem of the attitude of professional scientists like Helmholtz toward Mayer has been the subject of numerous studies by Ostwald and others. On net balance it appears that the professionals conceded to Mayer the public praise he deserved for his one great achievement, but would not bring themselves to think of him as a natural scientist in the exact sense. To them he was rather a "speculative" thinker. It is easy to see what they meant: Mayer's background in theoretical physics was poor and he handled mathematics with difficulty. He could hardly expect, therefore, to be considered on a par with Helmholtz and Kelvin in terms of overall accomplishment. But he was human enough to want credit for what he believed he had accomplished. It is now admitted that it was a very great accomplishment indeed.

As a matter of fact, honors came to Mayer in goodly measure in his later years. Among other things (and besides the award of the Copley medal of the Royal Society of London already mentioned) he was made an honorary doctor of philosophy of the University of Tübingen and a member of the Bavarian and Turin academies. After his death a momument was erected in his honor in his native city of Heilbronn.

Mayer's health had not been robust in the years following his nervous breakdown. Nevertheless, he was able to remain reasonably active until the winter of 1877–8 when he developed a tubercular infection in his right arm. He died on March 20, 1878.

In person Mayer was somewhat above the middle height. He had a large mouth and large ears. His eyes were dark brown in color and very expressive. However, he was nearsighted and had to wear spectacles all his life. He usually wore a light fringe beard. It is reported that when walking he always kept his gaze straight ahead. When sitting he had a tendency to bend forward. When interested he was animated in conversation but had no hesitation in expressing his boredom emphatically when the subject failed to excite his interest. Mayer spoke with a strong Swabian accent. However, he had a very clear and expressive German style, clearer in fact than that of many of his scientific contemporaries and successors. He tended to take a deep interest in religion and this grew stronger in his later years, particularly along fundamental lines. In this respect he somewhat resembled Faraday and evidently saw no conflict between his religious views and his scientific investigations.

PART II

Mayer's Contributions to Science

1. Review of the Concepts of Energy and Heat to the Time of Mayer

In order to appreciate the significance of Mayer's role in the generalization of the concept of energy it is desirable first to summarize briefly the evolution of this idea from the earliest times up to the period of Mayer's work. It is also essential to say something about the views of scientists concerning the nature of heat in the eighteenth and early nineteenth centuries in order to understand why it took so long for the mechanical theory of heat to gain general scientific acceptance.

The fundamental idea associated with the concept of energy is constancy in the midst of change. When our predecessors of some thousands of years ago first discovered the possibility of constructing a machine to take some of the sting out of human labor in moving heavy objects by using the application of a relatively small force to exert a much larger force, they must soon have noticed that Nature extorts a certain compensation in the action of such a device. This compensation consists in the fact that the product of the applied force by the distance through which the point of application moves is ideally equal in magnitude to the product of the exerted force by the distance through which its corresponding point of action moves. Thus the gain in force is compensated by the loss in distance moved. Or put in a more significant fashion, there is something that ideally at any rate remains constant during the change involved in the action of the machine, namely the product of force times displacement. This idea of constancy in the midst of change is the germ of the concept of energy.

The Aristotelian derivation of the law of the lever as a machine actually involved an appreciation of the constancy just described. Other demonstrations of the laws of machines by medieval scientists reflected

21

a similar understanding and this is well brought out by the later treatment of the law of the inclined plane by Galileo. The great French mathematician and philosopher Descartes emphasized constancy in the midst of change by stressing the importance of "quantity of motion" or what we now call momentum (the product of mass and velocity of a particle). He was much impressed by the invariance of the overall momentum in the case of the collision of particles and was led to the view that "force" in the interaction of particles is measured solely by change in momentum. This view was later challenged by the German Leibniz, who introduced the concept *vis viva* (living force) for the product of the mass of a particle by the square of its velocity, a scalar quantity, which unlike momentum, is independent of direction. Leibniz felt that the *vis viva* is the true measure of "force" in mechanics, the force that is connected with motion.

The Cartesian–Leibnizian controversy lasted nearly half a century (some historians think even longer), but a suggestion for its solution was at any rate made by D'Alembert in 1743 when he pointed out that the problem is really one of terminology. Change in momentum is a measure of the effect of force (in the Newtonian sense) over time, i.e., the time integral of the force, whereas change in *vis viva* is a measure of the effect of force over space, i.e., the space integral of the force.

Lagrange in his *Mecanique Analytique* (1787) followed up the *Leibnizian* scheme by showing that for certain mechanical systems of particles there exists a function of the positions and velocities of the particles with reference to some inertial system, a function which remains constant in time, no matter what the motions of the system may be. This function is the sum of two parts. The first part is one-half the sum of the *vis viva* values for all the particles. The second part is a function only of the relative positions of the particles. We now call the first part the total kinetic energy of the system of particles, whereas we call the second part the potential energy of the system. We now refer to the sum of the two parts as the total mechanical energy of the system. It must be emphasized that this notation was not used by Lagrange, nor was the word mechanical energy used in its current sense until around 1850. It was therefore not in use during the early and inventive part of Mayer's career.

Though the so-called conservation of *vis viva*, a misnomer for the conservation of total mechanical energy as the sum of the kinetic energy and potential energy (in modern terminology), was discussed at length by D'Alembert, Lagrange and other mathematical scientists of the eighteenth century as well as several in the early years of the nineteenth century, it was realized to be of limited value in the case of most terrestrial motions. It could certainly be successfully applied to celestial motions, but on earth came up against the all-pervading influence of frictional forces. A simple pendulum, once set going in air and left to itself ultimately comes to rest. What becomes of the mechanical energy originally given to it? If it disappears completely can there be any value at all in the principle which asserts its constancy during the change involved in the motion? Certainly something seemed to disappear and it was not clear that anything else happened to take its place. In those days this something was referred to as "force" (*Kraft* in German), and the idea that "force" could be destroyed as well as created was evidently not one repugnant to everyone. As we have seen in the biographical sketch, it clearly was to Mayer. Impressed by the concept of conservation of matter in chemistry, he felt that a similar idea should apply to an intangible effect like motion. We return to this in detail later.

At this place we recall the famous experiments of Benjamin Thompson, Count Rumford, in boring out cannon for the Elector of Bavaria in the last decade of the eighteenth century. Here there was an enormous expenditure of "force" or what we would call work or mechanical energy. At the same time, in addition to the obvious abrasion of the metal the production of large quantities of heat was observed. Rumford ultimately convinced himself that the appearance of this heat had much to do with the obvious loss of "force" or work. In fact he was sure that the motion used up was the source of the heat produced. Rumford had been led even earlier to assume that the heat in material substances is actually due to the vibratory motion of their constitutent particles. This early view of the mechanical theory of heat he may have

23

gotten from Hermann Boerhaave (1668–1738) whose treatise on chemistry (1732) suggested the vibratory nature of heat.

It might have been supposed that the work of Rumford and the suggestions of others would have firmly established the view that mechanical energy can be transformed into heat, thereby leading to the generalization of the concept of energy so as to assure its invariant character and its ability to represent constancy in the midst of change. That this result did not immediately ensue and that in fact the mechanical theory of heat was not firmly established for half a century after Rumford's famous experiments was doubtless due to the strong hold the caloric theory of heat had on the scientists of the eighteenth and early nineteenth centuries.

Caloric was the name given by the French chemist Lavoisier (1743–94) and his contemporaries at the end of the eighteenth century to heat treated as a substance, an idea that gained great currency in the earlier part of the century through the calorimetric experiments of Joseph Black. Caloric was assumed to be a substance which in our universe was finite in amount and could be neither created nor destroyed. It was weightless, self-repulsive and attracted by ordinary matter. It was able to penetrate within the spaces between the particles of matter and thus hold them apart against their natural gravitational attraction. Heating due to friction was ascribed to the squeezing out of the included caloric, thus making it free instead of latent. There was no known property of heat which could not receive at least a qualitative explanation in terms of the caloric theory. When Rumford protested that the supply of heat in his cannon-boring experiments was virtually inexhaustible, the adherents of the caloric theory could reply that there was always enough caloric stored in the metal and its surroundings to be transferred from the latent to the free state. The mechanical motion merely facilitated this transfer.

The arguments of the caloricists were so persuasive that it is after all not surprising that Rumford's views were not taken too seriously.

The action of a heat engine might indeed have given investigators a suspicion that the heat needed to run the engine probably had something to do with the "force" exerted, or as we should now say, the mechanical work done. But what really goes on in a heat engine was not fully appreciated until the epoch-making work of Sadi Carnot (1796–1832) in the early 1820s. In the early engines, heat merely served to make steam, which by its expansion moved the piston in the engine cylinder or by its condensation enabled atmospheric pressure to produce the appropriate motion. Hence the role of the heat was not too clear. Carnot in his famous 1824 memoir "Reflections on the Motive Power of Fire" clearly recognized the role of heat in the operation of an engine through the difference in temperature between the intake and exhaust of the working substance. What Carnot's view of the nature of heat was when he wrote his paper is uncertain. At the time it was believed by many competent critics that he adhered to the caloric theory. and that the proof of his celebrated theorem about the efficiency of engines, involving the assumption which later became known as the second law of thermodynamics, depended on this theory. On this basis, it was felt that he reasoned that just as water falling through a certain height can do work by turning a water wheel without using up any water, so heat in falling through a definite temperature range can also do work without changing its amount. The belief that Carnot used the caloric theory evidently lent considerable support to that theory during the first half of the nineteenth century. This provides a measure of the obstacles the supporters of the mechanical theory of heat like Mayer and Joule had to overcome.

We shall now see how Mayer tackled this problem.

2. Mayer's First Attempts at an Analysis of the Concept of Force

It has been pointed out in Part I that Mayer's observation of the color of venous blood in the Tropics stimulated his interest in the interrelations of natural phenomena. While there is no reason to doubt this statement, it must be admitted that in his early attempts to come to grips with this problem Mayer was guided more by philosophical considerations than by empirical facts. It is of some significance that in his first two papers (1841 and 1842) he makes no mention of his experience in the Tropics. References to this in his published writings do not occur before the 1845 and 1851 papers.

Mayer had studied enough chemistry to be impressed by the conviction of Lavoisier and his successors that in chemical reactions matter is conserved: it can neither be created nor destroyed, though it may change its form. Mayer early felt that the same sort of conservation ought to apply to forces as well. But to tackle this involved assigning a meaning to the concept of force. Mayer decided to say that forces are the causes of the changes that are observed in natural objects and their relations to each other. It should be emphasized that here Mayer consistently used the German word *Kraft* to designate what he was talking about. Here he was operating well within the physical science terminology of his time. In English-speaking countries it was customary during the eighteenth century and indeed a large part of the nineteenth century to refer to force as that which causes the appearance of all kinds of natural phenomena. It is true that Newton in his *Principia*, used the word force primarily in connection with motion. Nevertheless, terms such as electric force, magnetic force, static force, muscular force, heat force, etc., were common in the period in which Mayer was writing. The use of the term energy to replace this generalized force concept did not become widespread until some years after Mayer's epoch making work.

In Mayer's 1841 paper (unpublished) he emphasized his belief that forces as he conceived them (or energy as we should say today) are invariable in overall magnitude though variable in form. Thus he early had the strong feeling that all changes in natural phenomena are brought about by "force" (or energy) as a fundamental cause. In these processes the "force" may change its form but not its magnitude. "Force" (or energy) is indestructible and uncreatable.

In his first paper Mayer deliberately restricted his attention to changes represented by motion. This was a natural choice in view of the very significant role played by motion in the experience of human beings. But it was unfortunate that Mayer approached this problem with such an inadequate grasp of the principls of mechanics. He evidently realized the importance of momentum or mass times velocity, but thought

26

of it as a direct measuring of moving force, thus departing both from the Newtonian definition of force as well as from the notion of energy.

In applying the concept of momentum to examples that amount to collision of particles, Mayer seems to show some understanding of the principle of conservation of momentum, but fails to make accurate use of it because he evidently does not understand the significance of a vector quantity. He realizes that in inelastic collisions some part of the original motion disappears or is neutralized, as he puts it, but here fails to realize that this cannot be the momentum which is conserved independently of the character of the collision. This accounts for his floundering in a morass of bizarre and unconventional terminology, though after the event it is easy to see what he was driving at. Mayer is quite clear on the claim that the "lost" or neutralized "motion" reappears as heat in line with his conviction that motion is a "force" which can vary its form but cannot be destroyed or created. He also expresses the opinion that the heat produced is proportional to the motion that disappears, but in this first paper makes no effort to calculate the numerical relationship. He recognizes the possibility that heat may be transformed into motion in the expansion of bodies, evidently with the steam engine in mind, though he does not mention this case specifically. The breadth of his general grasp is indicated by the inclusion of radiant heat and light in his considerations.

An analysis of this 1841 manuscript makes it clear why it was not accepted for publication in a professional journal of physical science like that of Poggendorf. The physics was bad and the general emphasis on the interconnections of different physical effects was by no means entirely novel at the time. Yet Mayer's stress on the constant magnitude of "force" in the face of its variablity in form was a philosophical point of the greatest significance for the future of physics. Unfortunately it was almost completely concealed in the specific jargon of the paper.

It is probably idle to speculate what the effect on Mayer's future scientific career would have been had his paper actually been accepted and printed. Most authorities who have commented on this have expressed the strong opinion that he was very lucky his manuscript was turned down. According to this view the article, if published, would have been dismissed by professional scientists as the work of a crank and this would have discouraged Mayer to such an extent that he would not have ventured to develop his ideas further. However, in the light of what happened when he was able to break into print later, we cannot be too sure about this. It apparently took a great deal of neglect and adverse criticism to discourage Mayer.

3. Mayer's 1842 Paper and the Calculation of the Mechanical Equivalent of Heat

The bibliographical details concerning this article are given in Part III along with a new translation.

The paper shows a considerable and rather surprising improvement in Mayer's grasp of physical principles. This may have resulted from his detailed correspondence with Baur during the latter part of 1841.

Mayer still approaches the problem of the interrelation of natural phenomena from the broad philosophical viewpoint. As in his 1841 manuscript he treats "forces" as causes, but now invokes the famous principle laid down by Gottfried Wilhelm Leibniz that *causa aequat effectum* (The cause equals the effect). This principle appeared in an article published by Leibniz in 1690 entitled: "De Causa Gravitatis et Defensio Sententiae Autoris in Veris Naturae Legibus contra Cartesianos" (cf. G. S. Gerhardt's edition of Leibniz, vol. vi, p. 201). The relevant statement reads: "Ostendo aequationem latentum inter causam et effectum nulla arte violabilem esse" (I maintain that the latent equivalence between cause and effect is in no way violable). It is from this principle that Mayer deduces the law of the indestructibility of forces. A given force producing an effect takes the form of that effect and ceases to exist in its original form. At the same time the magnitude of the force in its original form is not destroyed; through some appropriate quantitative conversion factor it becomes the magnitude of the effect. This is the meaning Mayer ascribes to the word "equals" in Leibniz's principle. The principle is, of course, a hypothesis not without philosophical difficulties, but it suited Mayer's needs and he did not trouble himself to examine it more closely from a logical point of view.

Forces are not the only causes in our experience. Matter is also a cause. The distinction here is that forces are indestructible, transformable, and imponderable whereas matter is indestructible, transformable and ponderable. Mayer confines his attention in this article to force involved in free fall motion near the surface of the earth. The "force" that brings about the fall of an object he calls "fall-force" *(Fall-kraft)*. From the way he uses this quantitatively it is clear this is equivalent to the modern potential energy. In writing it he does set it equal simply to md, where m is the mass of the object and d its distance above the surface of the earth. He omits the acceleration of gravity g, presumably because he ignores the distinction between mass and weight, as was common in his time.

Mayer has now discovered Leibniz's *vis viva*, the product of the mass and the square of the instantaneous velocity. It is true he neglects the factor $\frac{1}{2}$ brought in by the space integration of the Newtonian force. He says that the *vis viva* is also a measure of the fall-force. He realizes that in line with his "cause equals effect" concept the fall-force measured by height of the object above the ground changes into fall-force measured by motion as *vis viva*; or as we should say, in falling there is a transformation of potential energy with kinetic energy.

Mayer is then faced with the problem: what happens when motion disappears and is not replaced by other motion or some other form of fall-force. His fundamental principle insists that no motion can be reduced to nothing; something must take its place and be evident to our senses. This something is ultimately heat. Mayer concentrates attention on the heat produced by friction in the rubbing of two metal plates together or in the violent shaking of water confined in a closed vessel. He realizes that to verify his thesis that all the "lost" motion reappears as heat, he must give attention to the further question: when heat has appeared as a result of the cessation of motion, have not other effects been produced besides heat? He must also naturally consider still another question: has not the heat in this case had another cause than motion? This is an honest appraisal of the situation.

29

Mayer states that only the most careful experimentation can settle the matter. Here he was certainly optimistic!

Mayer fails to mention at this point the easy solution of the adherents of the caloric theory of heat to the problem he raises: the only effect of the loss of motion in the rubbing experiment is the release of latent caloric from the rubbed substance or its surroundings. In fact, he makes no mention at all of the caloric theory in this essay. He does pay his respects to it in his 1851 paper, which we shall discuss later.

Mayer is on very shaky ground logically when he dismisses the possibility that any of the lost motion in a frictional experiment can find its way into a change in the state of aggregation of the material worked upon. In rubbing two metal plates together, some work is certainly done in polishing the surfaces, so that after rubbing the surfaces are not precisely in the same state as before rubbing began. It is true that the relatively enormous amount of heat developed by friction as compared with the observed change in the rubbed material lends considerable support to Mayer's thesis, and he evidently fully recognizes this. He seems to suggest indeed that other effects of the loss of motion in friction may occur, but he does not mention the obvious ones; namely electricity, sound and light. In later works he recognized this situation. But in the 1842 paper his mind is obsessed with the relation between motion and heat.

Mayer would have been on firmer ground in his fundamental hypothesis had he concentrated more attention on the illustration, which he introduces, of the rise in temperature of water shaken in a vessel. This was a favorite illustration of his. He seems to have done the experiment himself. Here he was thinking unwittingly along lines similar to Joule's ultimate choice of his paddle-box method of measuring the mechanical equivalent of heat. In this scheme, of course, some of the original lost motion of the shaker or stirrer goes to produce the large-scale motion of the water. But since this motion ultimately ceases, all ultimately goes into heat.

Mayer was much impressed with the production of heat by compression, by bringing, as he says, the particles of a substance closer together.

He finds an ingenious analogy here to the fall of an object to the earth, thus bringing things belonging to the earth closer together and also producing heat when the motion ceases on collision with the earth's surface.

That Mayer's view of the relation between heat and motion did not violate his interpretation of Leibniz's famous assertion about cause and effect is seen in his emphasis on the view that though the relation between heat and motion is fundamental, this does not mean that heat *is* motion. His two sentences here are worth quoting:

"From the relation connecting fall-force and motion we have no right to draw the conclusion that the essential nature of fall-force *is* motion, nor have we any greater right to draw this conclusion for heat. We should rather take opposite view that in order to become heat, motion (whether it be simple motion or vibratory motion like light or radiant heat) must cease to be motion."

It is clear that in this view Mayer parted company with Count Rumford, who as a result of his cannon-boring experiments in the last decade of the eighteenth century concluded that heat *is* a mode of motion. A very interesting point emerges here. In his well-known work *History and Root of the Principle of the Conservation of Energy* (English translation by P. A. B. Jourdain, Open Court Publishing Company, Chicago, 1911, p. 37) Ernst Mach quotes the above statement by Mayer with some satisfaction. Mach did not believe in the mechanical theory of heat and evidently interpreted Mayer's statement as a lack of belief in it also, at any rate in the form favored by Rumford and some others. It is worth emphasizing again that for Mayer to say that the cause equals the effect does not mean that the cause is the *same entity* as the effect, but that there is an equivalence in magnitude between them even though they differ in form. It is not apparent that Mach gave sufficient attention to this point; which is of the utmost importance in the development of thermodynamics, as recognized after Mayer's time by Helmholtz, Kelvin, Clausius and others.

Mayer calls attention to the heat generated by the fall of water in a mill operated by a water-wheel and again looks upon this as essentially due to the effective decrease in the volume of the earth when the water reaches the surface. He makes no mention of the mechanical energy used up in the work which the wheel does, but evidently is thinking of the residual energy of the water after leaving the wheel. On the other hand, he assumes that in the operation of a steam engine heat is transformed into motion. This was a view Mach was not willing to accept. He agreed that heat was necessary for the performance of work by a heat engine, but that the work resulted from the fall of the heat substance (caloric) from a high temperature to a lower temperature, just as in the water motor the work done is due to the fall of water from a height and does not involve any transformation of water into work.

Mayer winds up this paper with a statement of his conviction that there must be a definite quantitative relation between the quantity of heat required to raise the temperature of a given mass of water by 1 °C and the equivalent height to which this mass must be raised above the surface of the earth in order that by its fall from this height this quantity of heat will be produced. He then states that he has actually made the appropriate calculation by using the two specific heats of a gas, i.e., that at constant pressure and that at constant volume. Unfortunately he does not provide an explicit explanation of the details of his calculation, though it is now clear that his method must have led essentially to the standard equation

$$J = R/(c_p - c_v) \tag{1}$$

where R is the gas constant in energy units per gram per degree Celsius, and $c_p - c_v$ is the difference between the two specific heats of the gas in calories per gram per degree Celsius. The quotient is J, the mechanical equivalent of heat. The value for J given by Mayer corresponds essentially to what is obtained from this formula with the use of the somewhat uncertain values of c_p and c_v available to him.

It is difficult to understand why Mayer did not provide the details of his calculation. Actually he did so in his 1845 paper. But since he based his claim to priority on the theoretical estimate of J in the 1842 paper, it is unfortunate that only the barest outline of his method was provided there. There seems indeed no question that he knew what he was doing and why, but then why did he not say so in something more than half a page? Whether, indeed, this failure helped to rob him of the recognition he sought does remain uncertain, since even when his method was set forth in greater detail, serious criticism was leveled at it. This is discussed in connection with the critique of his subsequent work and in particular his 1845 essay.

4. The Broadening of Mayer's Ideas. Biological Application of the Concept of Energy

It was inevitable that Mayer, with his background in physiology and medicine, would seek to apply his viewpoint about the concept of energy to living organisms. This he did in his 1845 paper "The Motions of Organisms and their Relation to Metabolism—An Essay in Natural Science." It is a very extensive article, prefaced indeed by an elaboration of his earlier treatment of the relation between motion and heat and culminating in an expression of his conviction that the concept of energy and its possible transformations extends to all physical phenomena. It was indeed unfortunate that he did not make this extended development of his ideas in physics a wholly separate paper. This might well have secured for him the recognition of the value of his calculation of the mechanical equivalent of heat which was long denied. Privately printed, the paper seems to have attracted little attention, though Mayer made an earnest appeal in the first part of the paper that it should be carefully examined by professional physicists.

Mayer begins his essay by again emphasizing the essential philosophical basis of his theory. But he now exhibits a more effective grasp of the principles of mechanics and heat than was evident in his earlier work. It is true that he still employs the word "force" *(Kraft)* where we now use the word "energy", but this was common in the physical nomenclature of his time. The use of the word energy in the modern sense dates only from about 1860. In the translation of this essay in Part III, after the introduction the word *Kraft* is translated throughout by the term "energy".

Mayer shows a full appreciation of the way in which a steam engine works, in the transformation into mechanical energy of a part of the heat produced by the combustion of the fuel and the emission of the rest through the exhaust. It is clear he must have been familiar with the studies of Carnot. Mayer was also acquainted with the fundamental experiment of Gay-Lussac on the free expansion of a gas into a vacuum, which shows no perceptible change in temperature. This was crucial to his final assumption that the basic reason for the existence of the two specific heats of a gas is essentially the fact that in expanding at constant pressure the heat supplied to the gas must not only go to raise its temperature but also enable it to do work on its surroundings. Mayer then goes through the algebraic analysis which is essentially equivalent to that leading to the formula (1) given above. The value of J which Mayer calculated, namely 3.59 joules per calorie, is of course lower than the experimental value which Joule obtained at about the same time, namely 4.2×10^7 ergs per calorie. Mayer in his computation used the c_p value for air as first given by the French chemists, namely 0.265 calories per gram per degree C. He also used the ratio $c_p/c_v = 1.421$ to calculate c_v. Later Regnault showed that c_p actually is 0.238 and c_p/c_v is more nearly 1.40. With these values, Mayer's calculations yield a value for J in agreement with Joule's measured result.

It is clearly recognized by Mayer that his calculation is not limited to air but applies to any gas. He also proceeds to calculate the mechanical equivalent of the heat of combustion of carbon, to be used extensively in his later work.

It must be emphasized again and again that when Mayer states the fundamental principle "Heat equals mechanical energy", he in no sense means that heat *is* mechanical energy, but only that there is an equivalence in magnitude between a given quantity of heat measured in conventional heat units and a given quantity of mechanical energy, measured in work units. His terminology here may have confused some of his readers and engendered skepticism about his grasp of physics.

On the other hand, Mayer shows in this part of his 1845 paper that he has fully grasped the significance of the Cartesian–Leibnizian controversy on the relative merits of momentum versus *vis viva*, a matter he had evidently not understood in his 1841 manuscript.

Next follows the enumeration of the various phenomena of nature which can be interpreted in terms of energy transformation from one form to another while remaining constant in amount. These he discusses with a wealth of detail, indicating a thorough grasp of the scientific literature. His list includes potential energy, energy of motion *(vis viva)*, heat, electricity (both static and current), magnetism, and energy of chemical reactions. The thoroughness of his coverage reminds one of the more mathematical summary in Helmholtz's famous 1847 memoir "On the Conservation of Energy."

Mayer realizes that the chief source of energy on the surface of the earth is the radiation from the sun, past and present. This leads him at once to the problem of how this energy has been and is being utilized; this in turn serves as an introduction to the second and larger part of his essay, about two-thirds of the whole), which is devoted to the relation of energy to living things. It is not an exaggeration to say that this marks the first time when the concept of the transformation of energy was applied to biological phenomena. In a real sense it was the inauguration of what has come to be called biophysics. Though physiology and physiological chemistry were at the time well advanced on the continent of Europe, there was a genuine need for a unifying concept and this was precisely what Mayer supplied in his essay.

Prevalent at the time when Mayer was writing was the concept of "vital force", which was supposed to be exhibited by living things in order that they might carry on their functions. Mayer did his best to exorcise this notion of vitalism by stressing his conviction that its assumption would make impossible a genuinely scientific description of plant growth and behavior. He takes his stand firmly on the thesis that all vital processes are describable in terms of the transformation of matter and energy: in other words in terms of purely physical processes. Here Mayer demonstrates his feeling for the importance of the chemical reduction reactions involved in the action of sunlight on the plant as well as the oxidation reaction represented in the elimination of carbon dioxide.

Mayer was not content to leave the matter with these qualitative considerations. He felt it was necessary to estimate quantitatively the energy involved in metabolism—his pages teem with figures; he was extremely fond of arithmetic, which in general is accurate. Unfortunately he does not always reveal the source of his data. It was undoubtedly the heat he could obtain at the time, though he occasionally complains that figures are not precise enough to establish his case numerically beyond question.

After discussing in detail the physiology of plant life with special emphasis on the role of sunlight, Mayer turns to the animal kingdom which avails itself for living by taking advantage of the energy stored up in the plants. Here he begins by stressing the relatively great difference in mobility between animals and plants, leading to relatively vast expenditures of energy by animals in the mechanical form. It is interesting but hardly surprising that Mayer bases his unit of power on the activity of the average horse. However, his value for the horsepower is somewhat low by modern criteria, being equivalent in meter units to 720 watts instead of the arbitrarily chosen figure of 745 watts now used.

Realizing that the source of all the mechanical energy expended by living animals is the chemical energy involved in the consumption of food, but also realizing the inadequacy of current data on heats of combustion of food materials, he falls back on the heat of combustion of carbon and used the value due to Dulong, namely 8558 calories/gram which is about 7% higher than the modern accepted value. But this again hardly affects his fundamental conclusions.

Interesting estimates are provided as to the amount of equivalent carbon that must be bound in order to enable a man to carry out certain activities, including bowling, mountain climbing, etc. Mayer then carefully points out that these figures neglect the part of the energy expenditure that must go to supply the bodily heat.

Mayer discusses at some length the metabolism experiments of Dulong and Despretz, in which the claim was made that there is a lack of balance between the heat produced by the combustion of food and the bodily heat, with the definite implication that there exists a source of "vital" energy inside the living organism which is independent of any external agent. Mayer shows great keenness in locating flaws in the experiments of Dulong and Despretz, though his argument is of course colored by his very strong bias in favor of the energy conservation principle. He does not question the value of the experiments, but shows to his own satisfaction, at any rate, that the investigators really misinterpreted their results by failing to take into account every conceivable effect bearing on them. In a footnote reference to a contemporary work on physiology which adopts the vitalistic hypothesis, Mayer indulges in one of his rare exhibitions of sarcasm at the expense of the supporters of this viewpoint.

Much attention is paid to the relative proportions of the total heat produced by the oxidation of food represented in the observed bodily heat and the mechanical energy expended by an active individual. Both horses and men are considered and it is shown that in general the fraction of the available energy going into bodily heat is considerably greater than expended as mechanical energy. This to be sure applies primarily to large power expenditures. When work is done more slowly, the ratio of work to bodily heat produced is greater. As Mayer says, it pays to *make haste slowly!*

The next question is: how does the body transform the heat of combustion of the absorbed food into mechanical energy. This is done artificially in the heat engine, of which mankind has invented many varieties. Nature has provided the animal body with its own natural engine, namely the system of muscles. Mayer realizes that to explain the role of the muscles in the animal's mechanical activity, one most consider two aspects: (1) control, which assures that the organism does or endeavors to do what the nervous system directs, and (2) the source of the energy which the muscle is able to expend. The first is a motor nerve process and the second a part of the general metabolism. In his emphasis on the control of energy expenditure by the muscles, Mayer comes very close to introducing cybernetics into the physiological problem. This is effectively documented in his analogy between the organism and a steamship. The captain controls the direction of the ship's course by appropriate steering. The engineer, however, has to see that energy is provided to drive the ship. Both aspects are needed if the ship is to reach its desired destination.

The next question is: where does the muscle get the energy it has to expend? Mayer has no doubt that it must come from the combustion of organic material. He shows conclusively that this material cannot be the tissues of the muscles themselves. The special case of the heart provides a dramatic illustration. Mayer estimates that the mechanical energy expended by the heart in one day in pumping blood throughout the body has the heat equivalent of 1.158 calories, which involves the combustion of 13.5 grams of carbon. The heart could not last very long if it had to use up its own material in supplying this heat! Moreover, even if it is considered that bodily tissues can be removed if deteriorated or destroyed, this renewal process would not possibly take place fast enough to permit replacement of combustible material, if this material were to come from the tissues themselves.

There follows a rather long digression, of particular interest to Mayer as a medical man, on the living body's ability to resist decomposition and decay, but finally the author gets back on the track to consider the problem of the seat of the combustion in the body needed to provide the bodily heat. After a considerable discussion of physiological evidence, Mayer concludes that the heat is supplied by the oxidation of the blood. To quote him: "The blood, a slowly burning fluid, is the oil in the flame of life." He finds the blood corpuscles as the absorbers of the oxygen which gets into the body via the lungs, but that the oxidation process takes place in the fluid part of the blood—this is where the carbon dioxide and water are formed. The role of the surfaces of the blood vessels in this chemical activity is catalytic only, according to Mayer.

It is here that Mayer tells in some detail the story of his observation of the color of venous blood in the Tropics when he served as ship's doctor on his early trip to the East Indies, adding a few more or less relevant medical details to emphasize his understanding of the role of the blood corpuscles in the combustion process in the body. Mayer admits quite frankly that the precise mechanism leading to the transformation of chemical energy into mechanical energy in the muscles is a very complex affair. At his time it was largely unknown. Even today it is still considered a matter of great complexity and a subject for continual hypothesis—guided experiment. The role of oxidation in the blood is perhaps better understood now than in Mayer's time. It is now believed that oxidation plays a greater role in the recovery of muscle after mechanical energy expenditure than in the direct stimulus to this expenditure. Nevertheless, Mayer's treatment must be considered remarkable in its foreshadowing of later work on the transformation of energy in the animal body.

Mayer does reassure himself by some simple calculations based on the lifting activity of big muscles that the supply of chemical energy is fully adequate, indeed more than adequate to provide the necessary mechanical energy as determined from the mechanical equivalent of heat. This leaves plenty over for the supply of bodily heat. It also emphasizes that the efficiency of the body "engine" in its transformation of heat into work, like that of the heat engines constructed by man working on thermodynamic principles, is always considerably less than 100%.

The predominant role of the heart, as in many ways the most important muscle in the animal body, is stressed. Moreover, calculations, are presented to confirm the supposition that though the short-term expenditure of energy by a given muscle depends on its mass, the long-term ability to expend energy is a function wholly of the mass of the circulating blood.

Mayer anticipates the more modern emphasis on the "wisdom of the body" by the way in which increased rate of breathing, increased muscular activity and accelerated blood circulation respond to increased demands for energy expenditure involved in violent exercise. Here again there is a foreshadowing of the cybernetics of the organism.

Mayer's zeal for applying the physical principles of the mechanical theory of heat to the physiology and mechanical behavior of the body led him to develop an analogy between the expansion of gases and their performance of work on the one hand and the so-called irritability of muscles in their transformation of chemical energy into mecha-nical energy on the other. He writes the first law of thermodynamics for a gas in the usual form, whereby when a quantity of heat is supplied to a gas, part goes to increase the temperature and the rest enables the gas to do work against its surroundings. He recognizes that the work done by the gas is dimensionally given by the product of pressure and volume, but his precision of expression is poor and by no means as careful as in his biological statements. One might have supposed that by this stage he would have acquired enough grasp of simple theoretical physics to realize that the work is $\int p\,dV$, where p is the instantaneous pressure and dV the change in volume. He quotes Boyle's law for the relation between pressure and volume of a gas, but implies that it holds for all changes and not merely the isothermal ones. He then goes on to see the physiological analog of Boyle's law in that of Theodor Schwann, viz. the tension in a muscle varies inversely as the increase in its contraction. The analogy is fundamentally sound, but it is a pity that Mayer shows himself so shaky in his physics in establishing it.

Mayer assumes that the measure of permanent irritability of a muscle is given by the minimum amount of oxygen needed to excite it. Here he is probably somewhat out of line with modern developments of the subject in view of what was said above about the direct role of oxygen in the immediate supply of energy for muscular activity. At any rate he feels that some muscles can stay active longer without renewal of the oxygen supply: they exhibit a kind of "permanent" irritability. Other muscles fatigue more rapidly. This Mayer connects with the size of the blood corpuscles: the larger the corpuscles, the greater the ability to take up oxygen and the greater the "permanent" irritability.

Much attention is paid to the efficiency of the animal organism, in analogy with the efficiency of heat engines. It is pointed out that the average efficiency of a mammal (i.e., the ratio of useful mechanical energy which can be expended to the total heat produced by combus-tion in the animal) is around 20%, though it is not clear where this figure is obtained. The larger the chemical activity in the body with the correspondingly large production of carbon dioxide, the smaller the efficiency, which is also connected with the largest "permanent" muscular irritability. Interestingly enough, the fishes and other cold-blooded animals show greater efficiency than the warm-blooded mammals because they do not need to devote so much of the heat energy produced in the body to maintaining a high blood heat. Presumably this makes them better fitted to expend the mechanical energy necessary to move through the water easily in spite of the resistance it offers to the motion of solids.

Mayer admits that his analogy between the behavior of the animal organisms and that of heated gas in the conventional heat engine ultimately breaks down, though he does not go into details on this point. He is indeed led to speculate about the possibility of constructing what he calls "cold-blooded" engines with higher efficiency than those common in his day. It is hard to tell here whether he is thinking of engines in which the exhaust takes place at very low temperature. Indeed nowhere in his 1845 article does he indicate any appreciation of the second law of thermodynamics or even of the thermodynamic expression for the efficiency of a heat engine in terms of the difference in temperature between intake and exhaust. It is curious that he would not have studied carefully the work of Carnot a quarter of a century before.

Mayer realizes that it is impossible to understand the mechanical behavior of the animal organism without the introduction of muscular control and this he finds clearly enough in the nervous system. The nerves cannot supply energy to the muscles to enable the latter to do work, but they can tell the muscles when to work, how much to do and when to stop. In this process the nervous system acts like a kind of governor, which employs a small amount of the energy produced by chemical means to control the relatively large amount expended by the muscles. Mayer here is obviously using the fundamental notions of cybernetics and feedback, a full century before Norbert Wiener, though well after James Watt and his steam engine governor. He shows no indication of being familiar with the pioneer work in the 1830s of Ampere, who actually first coined the term *cybernetique*, though he applied it to government rather than to living organisms and mechanical devices.

The discussion of muscular fatigue with which Mayer closes his 1845 paper is illuminated by the clear distinction he draws between fatigue due to exertion and that owing to mechanical energy expenditure. He emphasizes that it is only when the animal organism does work in the physical sense, i.e., raises weight or communicates kinetic energy to objects , that the fatigue of its muscles must be overcome by the further intake of food to supply fuel for the bodily engine. Mere exertion, such as *supporting* a weight at rest does not involve energy expenditure. The resulting fatigue is taken care of by resting and has nothing to do with the intake of food. He of course excludes exertion of such a magnitude as to produce a pathological condition.

Mayer marvels at the complexity of life, but feels that he has made certain aspects of it, at any rate, more understandable in terms of the great principle of energy.

5. Mayer's Further Excursion into the Physical Domain. The Heat of the Sun and of the Earth

Not contented with the biological applications of the energy principle in his 1845 paper, Mayer determined to look more closely at physical problems in which the principle might be of use. It is not surprising that his attention was attracted to the question of the origin of the sun's heat. This was in the middle of the nineteenth century an astronomical puzzle of the first order. It was, of course, closely connected with the problem of the age of the sun and hence of the solar system and was of cosmological importance. Mayer had evidently made himself familiar with the relevant literature on celestial mechanics and had become more competent to handle physical calculations. Much of this increased grasp of physical ideas was probably due to his intimate association with Baur.

The speed and intensity with which Mayer worked at this period are made evident by the fact that in 1846 he sent an article "Sur la production de la lumiere et de la chaleur du soleil" to the Academy of Sciences in Paris. The paper was not published, nor was there any answer. This material was worked over and enlarged so that a substantial essay was published in 1848 with the title "Beiträge zur Dynamik des Himmels in Populäron Darstellung." Once again Mayer fell back on private publication. The article was brought out by the Verlag von Johann Ulrich Landherr in Heilbronn: Bibliographical details and a translation are given in Part III.

Mayer begins by observing that the radiation of light from the sun implies a continual loss of energy. From the conservation principle, this energy must come from somewhere; presumably heat. The question then is, what sources of heat are available in the sun? Mayer then enumerates the possible sources of heat known in his day: chemical, electrical and mechanical. The prime omission was of course radioactivity and nuclear reactions of which he could know nothing since these phenomena and theories were a half a century or more in the future. But immediately an interesting philosophical question arises: Might it not have been expected that a man of Mayer's creative imagination would have referred at least speculatively to the possibility that new sources of heat would be uncovered during the years ahead? It may well be an unfair question, and yet we know that a scientist like Faraday exhibited this kind of uncanny prescience with respect to the future possibilities of electric discharges through gases at low pressure. On the other hand, even a quarter century after the discovery of radioactivity and the invention of the atomic nucleus, scientists working in this very field were extremely skeptical about its promise as a source of energy. We must not be too hard on Mayer!

Mayer confines his attention to combustion on the chemical side, though he recognizes that the fundamental action of the voltaic cell is a chemical process. And in his arithmetic with respect to combustion his figures relate exclusively to coal. It is curious he did not consider hydrogen, though from an order of magnitude standpoint the difference is hardly material. On the mechanical side Mayer of course reviews the mechanical theory of heat and quotes the value of the mechanical equivalent of heat he obtained in 1842, namely the equivalent of 3.67 joules/calorie. It is strange that he did not use Joule's experimentally obtained value, since by this time he must have become acquainted with Joule's work. However, here again the precise figure is not too important for the use he makes of it.

Mayer's estimate of the solar radiation is far out of line with current estimates, since the value of the solar constant (the average amount of radiation reaching the earth's surface per square centimeter per minute) which was available in his day was only about one-fifth that accepted today. Here again the exact figures are not important. The total solar radiation is so enormous that Mayer felt sure some replenishment of this energy loss was absolutely necessary to account for the long time during which the radiation has endured. He very easily shows that if chemical processes alone are at work even supposing enough oxygen were available to support combustion, the whole of the sun might be burned up in only a matter of 5000 years. He concludes, therefore, that some mechanical action must be responsible.

Mayer does not overlook the energy involved in the rotation of the sun as its axis. But he realizes that this could hardly be transformed into heat without friction and he sees nothing for the sun to rub against as it rotates. He ignores the possibility of relative motion of various layers of the sun's gases. In any case even the whole kinetic energy of the sun, supposing it rotates as a single body, would not supply its radiated output for more than 183 years! So Mayer decides to examine the heat-producing potentiality of objects falling into the sun from outer space. The astronomers assure him that there is a lot of matter besides the planets and the sun in the solar system. All this cosmic material moves about the sun in orbits which are conic sections. But Mayer also believes firmly in the existence of an aether of space, a medium pervading all space in which the cosmic motions must take place and which provides resistance to this motion, so that ultimately all the material revolving about the sun must fall into it. The meteorites which fall to the earth in such numbers must be duplicated in vastly increased ratio by those that fall into the sun. So here is a ready-made answer to the problems of the heat of the sun.

Mayer was familiar with what we now call the energy equation for a particle moving in a gravitational field, that is, the equation which puts the sum of the kinetic and potential energies of the particle equal to the total mechanical energy. He then calculates with impeccable arithmetic the ideal velocity with which a particle falling from infinity along a straight line toward the earth will strike the earth. This is, of course, equal to the "escape" velocity or about 11.2 km/sec. He carries out the same computation for a particle striking the sun and obtains 630.4 km/sec. The generalization to a particle moving in an elliptical orbit about the sun follows naturally and the velocity attained when the particle's distance from the center of the sun becomes equal to the radius of the sun is readily computed.

The next step is to estimate the heat produced when the kinetic energy attained on striking the sun's surface is all transformed into heat. Mayer uses his value of the mechanical equivalent of heat to express this in terms of the impact velocity v in calories per gram as follows

$$1.39 \times 10^{-4} v^2.$$

The modified value with the correct value for the mechanical equivalent of heat is

$$1.19 \times 10^{-4} v^2.$$

Mayer's terminology here is somewhat confused. He consistently talks in terms of degrees of heat. If he means degrees of temperature, his result has meaning only if the specific heat capacity of the falling object is specified. If he means calories, it must be per gram of material independent of the specific heat. He probably meant the latter.

Since Mayer considers his essay a popular presentation, he supplements the above numerical discussion with a review of the evidence in ordinary human experience for the production of heat by the expenditure of mechanical energy and devotes much space to analogies relating great things with small. He treads at times on rather shaky philosophical ground as when he argues that the essence of all laws of nature is their universal range. This indeed worked well when Newton (according to the old story) generalized from the motion of an apple on the surface of the earth to the motion of the planets around the sun. Unfortunately, modern physics has shown that the principles of mechanics that describe rather well the behavior of so-called large-scale objects at velocities well below the velocity of light do not apply

45

when applied to the constituents of atoms. Here again we should not be too hard on Mayer. Hindsight is much better than foresight, even with respect to the philosophy of physics.

Mayer was able to show that the kinetic energy of an object falling into the sun will when transformed into heat produce more mass for mass than will result from any conventional chemical reaction. This convinced him that the meteoric theory of the origin and maintenance of the sun's heat was the correct one. However, there is nothing in his article to indicate any reasonable astronomical justification for the existence of the enormous numbers of meteors necessary to supply the necessary heat. He merely assumes that the universe is so full of this cosmic debris that there is plenty available for the purpose he has in mind. He does carry out a calculation showing that to maintain the sun's heat enough meteoric mass must fall on the sun yearly to increase its mass sufficiently to decrease the periods of revolution of the planets by an amount which should be observable. Mayer admits that such decrease has not been observed and hence to maintain his theory must fall back on the assumption that the sun loses mass through its radiation, a kind of anticipation, though without additional justification, of the Einstein mass–energy relation.

Subsequent study has led to the conclusion that Mayer's meteoric hypothesis is untenable, largely on quantitative grounds: there is no good astronomical ground for supposing that of the cosmic debris available, enough actually strikes the sun per unit time. In any case if it did, it is hard to see why the earth would not be bombarded by a proportionate number of such sizes as to render our planet too hot for life.

Interestingly enough, Lord Kelvin (then Sir William Thomson) independently introduced the meteoric theory of the sun's heat in 1853. At that time he appears not to have been aware of Mayer's work, but later acknowledged Mayer's priority. Kelvin later abandoned the theory in favor of the gravitational contraction process first suggested by Helmholtz in 1854 in a lecture given in Königsberg on "The Interaction of Natural Forces." In this lecture Helmholtz made reference to Mayer as one of the founders of the principle of conservation of energy, and acknowledged his priority in this matter over Joule, Colding and himself. He made no mention, however, of Mayer's theory of the sun's heat. Helmholtz approaches this problem from the standpoint of the Kant–Laplace nebular hypothesis of the origin of the solar system. Helmholtz showed that as a mass of gas contracts under mutual gravitational attraction, mechanical energy will be transformed into heat. His calculations, admittedly specialized in character, indicated that this is a more plausible theory of the sun's heat than Mayer's meteoric theory. Much subsequent work was done on the contraction theory, extending even into the early years of the twentieth century. However, even with the most favorable boundary conditions and assumptions as to the composition of the sun, the rate of heat development on this theory has never met the cosmological age requirements. As is well known, the present theory of solar heat is that based on the energy transformation involved in nuclear reactions and specifically in the heat liberated in the formation of helium nuclei out of hydrogen.

So far as is known, Mayer did not consider the gravitational contraction hypothesis as a basis for explaining the heat of the sun. This is curious, since in his earlier work he often stressed the development of heat due to the decrease in volume of an object. As a matter of fact, in his chapter on the internal heat of the earth in the essay under discussion he indicates a complete understanding of the basic idea underlying gravitational contraction when he says:

"Newton's theory of gravitation while it enables us to determine, from its present form, the earth's state of aggregation in ages past, at the same time points out to us a source of heat powerful enough to produce such a state of aggregation, powerful enough to melt worlds; it teaches us to consider the molten state of a planet as a result of the mechanical union of cosmical masses, and thus derive the radiation of the sun and the heat in the bowels of the earth from a common origin."

The above quotation makes us wonder why Mayer did not choose to supplement his meteoric theory of the origin of the sun's heat with

47

the contraction hypothesis. A possible reason may have been his inadequate grasp of the mathematics needed for the working out of the details of such a theory. The question remains why Helmholtz in his 1854 lecture failed to mention Mayer's obvious understanding of the basic idea of the contraction hypothesis. By this time Mayer's 1848 paper must have come to his attention. This overlooking or disregard of the scientific achievements of one's scientific contemporaries is one of the basic problems in the sociology of science; it has been the theme of countless commentators, who have done their best to provide reasons for the curious behavior of eminent scientists, without in general too much success. The larger problem of priority in scientific discovery though ideally soluble in an abstract sense in terms of publication date, remains in its essence hopeless. The history of science rests ultimately on arbitrary decisions.

Of the remaining chapters of Mayer's 1848 essay beyond that connected with the heat of the sun, the most interesting are those relating to the tides and the internal heat of the earth. Mayer was one of the first if not the first to point out the effect of the tides through friction on the rotation of the earth and asserted boldly that the result is a steady diminution of the earth's rotational velocity. Mayer even presents some simplified calculations based on what he deems to be a reasonable minimum value of the tidal frictional force at the earth's equator and concludes that in 2500 years the length of the day due to this cause has increased by about 0.06 sec. The problem was attacked in more elaborate mathematical detail by the British mathematician and astronomer J. C. Adams in the period from 1853 to 1859. Still later in 1879 G. H. Darwin in England made another study of the problem and concluded that the lengthening of the day due to tidal friction could not be greater than about 6×10^{-4} sec in 2500 years. This value is only 1/100 of that roughly estimated by Mayer, but the latter must be considered to have been somewhere near the ball park! He does indeed hedge by pointing out that his result depends on the temperature of the earth.

The final consideration of interest in Mayer's 1848 essay is his speculation concerning the internal heat of the earth. Mayer takes it for granted that the earth began its existence as a separate entity as a very hot object and has been cooling off ever since. This, however, from the physical characteristics of solid bodies, means that the volume of the earth is shrinking as it cools. This brings about a decrease in the moment of inertia of the earth about its axis of rotation and hence an increase in the angular velocity of rotation. This would serve to shorten the day. Yet he calls attention to the fact that Laplace estimated that the length of the day has not changed appreciably (i.e., not more than 1/500 sec) in 2500 years. To reconcile the two results would require some mechanism for lengthening the day. Mayer naturally would like to see tidal friction in this role. Curiously enough, however, he sees no particular inconsistency between his estimate of the lengthening of the day due to tidal friction and the Laplace result. Nor does Mayer have anything to say about the change in the length of the day due to purely gravitational causes as estimated by Laplace, Delauney, Adams and others. It is clear that throughout his work Mayer was obssessed with phenomena directly involving energy transformations. Of course, in connection with the internal heat of the earth he completely overlooks the possibility of sources of heat in the earth, such as we now associate with radioactivity and nuclear reactions.

6. The Summing Up. Mayer's Last Important Work on the Concept of Energy

Mayer's chief contribution to the establishment of the concept of energy in physical and biological science ended with the publication of his 1848 paper. Little if any formal recognition of his work had developed. In spite of this Mayer continued his reading of the current literature bearing on heat and work and evidently sought for further evidence of the value of the energy concept in science. The years 1848 on were times of increasing nervous strain. Mayer became involved in the revolutionary movement which disturbed southern Germany in 1848 and 1849, leading to disruption in his own family and great embarrassment if not actual danger to himself. Two of his children died in 1848. His feelings were exacerbated by the unfortunate Seyffer incident already referred to in Part I. Added to all this must have been the frustration involved in the feeling that his work was being wholly ignored. Rather surprisingly in view of all this Mayer found occasion to bring out a fifth paper of some length "Bemerkungen über das mechanische aequivalent der Wärme" (Comments on the mechanical equivalent of heat) printed privately by the Verlag von Johann Ulrich Landherr of Heilbronn in 1851. This paper is a kind of summary review in relatively nontechnical language of Mayer's own estimate of the significance of what he had done. Although it contains little in the way of new ideas about the conservation of energy, it is worth inspecting for the light it sheds on the development of Mayer's philosophical leanings. It foreshadows indeed some of the important controversies that marked the discussion of the nature of physical concepts during the latter part of the nineteenth century.

On the philosophical side Mayer would probably have classified himself as an empiricist or positivist, since he never lost an opportunity to stress the importance of exact acquaintance with the physical phenomena before indulging in too much speculation. To him thorough knowledge about a phenomenon was finally equivalent to the "truth" as distinct from the hypothesis which was not, so to speak, so clearly present in the phenomenon that its validity could not be denied. Mayer, like many other great thinkers who have hit on a successful idea, failed to see the hypothetical essence of his own scientific thinking. To him the concept of energy was not a hypothesis—it was simply the true way to look upon a large part of human experience.

To illustrate his feeling about the failure of hypothetical reasoning too far removed from the facts, Mayer singles out Aristotle for special attack. He considers the Aristotelian attempt to deduce the law of the lever inept because of its obsessive dependence on the mathematical properties of the circle. Mayer's reading of history here went off the track. Ironically the Aristotelian method of approaching the law of the lever was based essentially on the assumption of the principle of virtual work and hence contained within itself the germ of the idea of mechanical energy, the very concept which Mayer was so successful in generalizing. But Mayer's grasp of physics was not great enough to appreciate the significance of the historical development of the concept. He should not be criticized for this.

Mayer stamps himself as in some sense a follower of the ancient Pythagorean philosophy in his insistence on the importance of *numbers* in science. Like Lord Kelvin he felt that unless you could measure a thing and attach a number to it you could not hope to understand it. In his 1851 essay he gives many examples. Why was astronomy (which he considers the most difficult of all the sciences) so successful in antiquity? This came about because the early astronomers realized the need of attaching precise numbers to their observations. Why did chemistry finally become a science? This was because the chemists decided to weigh substances with great precision and express their results numerically. So combustion, for example, became a chemical phenomenon which could be compared successfully with other phenomena in numerical terms. This leads at once to concern for the precise measurement of quantity of heat, involving accurate temperature measurement. So finally Mayer gets around again as in all his papers to the problem of the relation between heat and motion.

He recites at some length the story of his blood color observation made in Java. There is a review of the biological significance of the energy idea, largely based on his 1845 paper: Mayer recalls how he was led to seek in physics a fundamental basis for the relation between heat and motion and stresses that his search was assisted by the use of the fundamental philosophical principle: *From nothing comes nothing*. This led directly to his conviction that there must exist a numerical mechanical equivalent of heat, whose evaluation he finally achieved in 1842 by his study of the two specific heats of gases. Interestingly enough he does not provide a complete outline of his method. Perhaps he felt that the development given in his 1845 paper was enough. In view of the central importance of this deduction in his whole scientific achievement it is unfortunate that he did not review the detailed derivation in this summary essay.

Mayer's penchant for the philosophical and methodological aspects of science is further exemplified by the detailed study he presents of the problem of terminology in mechanics. He shows a clear recognition of the embarrassing situation inherent in the ambiguous use of the word "force" (*Kraft* in German). In Mayer's time it had two different meanings in mechanics. The first was the Newtonian one, popularly expressed in terms of pushes and pulls, while the second was the one Mayer and others used to denote motion or changes in position, what we call today kinetic and potential energy. Mayer realized that different terms should be employed for these two different concepts in order to avoid confusion, but somehow he could not bring himself to invent a new term for his brand of force, which was the way the problem was solved later in the nineteenth century by Kelvin and Rankine. It is clear that Mayer was not happy with the Newtonian concept of force. He felt that as developed by the successors of Newton it was too mathematical. It involves derivatives and Mayer shunned calculus. On the other hand, kinetic energy and potential energy (motion and fall-force, as he called them) are simple algebraic expressions usable correctly by anyone in simple mechanical problems. Mayer's inadequate grasp of analytical mechanics misled him badly here. However, he deserves great credit for having clearly grasped the importance of the nomenclature problem. Here he foreshadowed the great controversies over the meaning and definition of the concepts of mechanics associated with the names of Hertz, Mach, Poincaré, Duhem, Pearson and others toward the end of the nineteenth century. It took a long time to reach a concensus on these matters, and a casual look into some current texts in elementary physics makes one wonder whether the problem is clearly understood by teachers of physics even today.

Mayer goes to some pains to reassert his earlier conviction that though motion and heat are equivalent this does not mean they are the same thing (i.e., that heat *is* motion). He quotes a paragraph from his 1842 paper to this effect, a statement which incidentally was also quoted years later by Ernst Mach in his polemic against the mechanical theory of heat in its atomic form. This is another irony in the history of science.

Mayer was clearly much concerned with the problem of the nature of heat and devotes much attention to it in his 1851 paper. He is unwilling to accept the caloric theory and dismisses it as emphatically as did Rumford a halfcentury before. At the same time he cannot bring himself to believe in the atomic theory of heat. He is clearly on the fence with regard to the value of the atomic hypothesis in physics, though he readily admits its great merit in chemistry. So he practically gives up the attempt to explain the real nature of heat associated with change in temperature or free heat as he calls it. On the other hand, latent heat is a cause of rejoicing to him as it fits in so well with his own conceptions of the transformability of work into heat and vice versa.

At the end of the 1851 paper Mayer pays his respects to the important work of Joule and recites with admiration Joule's many contributions to the relation between heat and motion. He does get in one subtle indirect dig at Joule for having criticized earlier Mayer's 1842 calculation of the mechanical equivalent of heat on the ground that Mayer's assumption that the latent heat represented in the difference between the two specific heats of a gas goes into work would not be justified until it was shown experimentally that when a gas expands into a vacuum no temperature change in observed, a result which Joule thought he was the first to observe. Mayer reminds the reader that Gay-Lussac observed this effect long before Joule and that he, Mayer, was aware of the French chemist's work.

The 1851 paper refers to a device which Mayer says he constructed in order to measure the mechanical equivalent of heat. Mayer does not describe the details of the apparatus nor how he used it, but from what he says it is likely it involved the continuous pumping of water through a narrow tube and the measurement of the power exerted and the rise in temperature of the water. The device is now in the Mayer archives of the City of Heilbronn. A picture and description are given in *Robert Mayer. Sein Leben and Werk in Dokumenten* by Helmut Schnolz and Hubert Weckbach, published by Anton H. Konrad Verlag, Heilbronn 1964, p. 64. There is still no clear indication of how the apparatus worked, but it is of great interest, since it appears to be the only reference in a major publication of Mayer to experimental equipment constructed by him in connection with his work on the energy concept.*

The 1851 paper concludes with an explanation of the phenomena exhibited by shooting stars in terms of the transformation of frictional work into heat. There is also a hint of the role of energy transformation in the appearance of new stars. Curiously there is no mention here of his theory of the origin and maintenance of the sun's heat. It would be interesting to know whether at this time he still held to his meteoric theory of the heat of the sun.

The publication of the 1851 paper marks the end of Mayer's chief contributions to the mechanical theory of heat and the generalization of the concept of energy. The years succeeding this date were marred by ill health. Though after his recovery he wrote some papers and indeed revived his interest in scientific matters, nothing essentially new emerged to add to his reputation in the field to which he had contributed so much as an essentially young man.

The bibliography which follows provides some indication of the scientific interests of his last years.

---

* More recently it has been established with considerable probability that the device mentioned in this paragraph, though undoubtedly developed by Mayer, was not intended to measure the mechanical equivalent of heat but rather human blood pressure. (See Helmut Schmolz: "Das Ratsel um eine Maschine im naclass Robert Mayers" in *Schwaben und Franken* (Heimatge-schichtliche Beilage der *Heilbronner Stimme*, Vol. 15, No. 11, November 8, 1969)).

It may be mentioned that a device for measuring the mechanical equivalent of heat constructed on more conventional Joulean lines and said to have been Mayer's is on view in the Deutsches Museum in Munich.

Bibliography

1. "Über die quantitative und qualitative Bestimmung der Kräfte" (1841). This paper was not accepted for publication in Poggendorf's *Annalen der Physik und Chemie*. It was later retrieved and published as follows:
   ZOLLNER, *Wissenschaftliche Abhandlungen* (Vol. IV, Leipzig, 1881, p. 680).
   J. J. WEYRAUCH, *Kleinere Schriften und Briefe von Robert Mayer* (Stuttgart, Cotta, 1893, p. 100).
   It is published in English translation in the present volume.
2. "Bemerkungen über die Kräfte der unbelebten Natur" (*Liebig's Annalen der Chemie und Pharmacie*, Vol. 42, p. 239 (1842)).
3. *Die organische Bewegung in ihrem Zusammenhang mit dem Stoffwechsel. Ein Beitrag zur Naturkunde* (Heilbronn, Verlag der C. Drechlerschen Buchhandlung, 1845).
4. *Beiträge zur Dynamik des Himmels in populäre Darstellung* (Heilbronn, Verlag von Johann Ulrich Landherr, 1848).
5. *Bemerkungen über das mechanische Aquivalent der Wärme* (Heilbronn, Verlag von Johann Ulrich Landherr, 1851).
6. "Über das Fieber. Ein iatromechanischer Versuch" (*Arkiv der Heilkunde*, 1862, p. 385).
7. "Über temporare Fixsterne" (*Das Ausland*, Vol. 38, No. 37, p. 865, 1866).
8. "Über notwendige Konsequenzen und Inkonsequenzen der Wärmemechanik" (*Tagblatt der 43. Versammlung deutscher Naturforscher und Arzte in Innsbruck*, 1869, No. 3, p. 40).
9. "Über Kraftmesser" (*Tagblatt der 43. Versammlung deutscher Naturforscher und Arzte in Innsbruck*, 1869, No. 4, p. 63).
10. "Über Auslösung" (Aufsatz in der *Besonderen Beilage des Staatsanzeigers für Würtemberg* (March 22, 1876)).

   Note: This bibliography does not include references to unpublished lectures and material in newspaper articles. For fuller details on these, consult the book of Schmolz and Weckbach referenced in the following list.

Selected works about Julius Robert Mayer

1. O. BLACK: "Value of inspiration—a study of J. R. Mayer" (*Isis*, Vol. 43, p. 211 (1952)).
2. E. DÜHRING: *Robert Mayer, der Galilei des neunzehnten Jahrhunderts. Eine Einführung in seine Leistungen und Schicksale* (Chemnitz, Verlag von Ernst

Schmeitzner, 1880). II. *Neues Licht über Schickal und Leistungen* (Leipzig, Druck und Verlag von C. G. Naumann, 1895).

3. ERNST JENTSCH: *Julius Robert Mayer. Seine Krankheitsgeschichte und die Geschichte seiner Entdeckung* (Berlin, Verlag von Julius Springer, 1914).

4. WILHELM OSTWALD: *Grosse Männer* (Leipzig, Akademische Verlagsgesellschaft m.b.H., 1909, pp. 61–100).

5. HELMUT SCHMOLZ and HUBERT WECKBACH: *Robert Mayer. Sein Leben und Werk in Dokumenten* (Heilbronn, Anton H. Konrad Verlag, 1964).

6. J. J. WEYRAUCH: *Kleinere Schriften und Briefe von Robert Mayer* (Stuttgart, Cotta, 1893).

Die Mechanik der Wärme (Stuttgart, Cotta, 1893).

PART III

On the Quantitative and Qualitative Determination of Forces

Editorial Preface

So far as is known, this is the first scientific paper by Mayer on the subject of energy. It was submitted to Poggendorf's *Annalen der Physik und Chemie* with a covering letter dated June 16, 1841. This was only five months after his return to Heilbronn from his voyage to the East Indies and indicates his strong desire to have his ideas on "forces" brought to the attention of the scientific public. This manuscript was not accepted for publication and was never returned to the author in spite of repeated requests. Thirty-six years later it was retrieved by Zöllner and published [Zöllner, *Wissenschaftliche Abhandlungen*, Vol. IV, Leipzig, 1881, p. 680]. It was later published in J. J. Weyrauch, *Kleinere Schriften and Briefe von Robert Mayer*. Stuttgart, Cotta, 1893, p. 100.

The paper is reproduced here, in spite of its technical shortcomings, precisely because it was Mayer's first attempt to set forth his ideas for public examination. It manifests an inadequate grasp of physical principles and introduces a bizarre terminology which would naturally repel the physicists and chemists of Mayer's time. Nevertheless, it represents an earnest attempt to handle the problem of interconversion of natural phenomena which was uppermost in Mayer's mind. It contains flashes of insight which were translated into effective results in later work. So far as is known, this is the first English translation of the paper. It is by the author of this book.

The first document of a great scientific thinker, no matter how halting, inconclusive or even erroneous, deserves an important place in the history of science.

IT IS the task of natural science to explain the phenomena of both the inorganic and the organic worlds in terms of their causes and effects. All phenomena rest on the fact that matter, bodies and their relations to each other are subject to changes. From the laws of logical reasoning we assume that this cannot happen without a cause. This cause we call force. [The German word here is *Kraft*. In this article we shall translate it by the word *force*, though in later articles it will be more in accordance with modern terminology to use the word *energy*—Ed. note.] If, in following the causal chain, we encounter phenomena the causes of which are no longer perceptible to the senses, but can be determined only by their effects, we shall call these forces abstract forces in the narrow sense. We can derive all phenomena from a primeval force which has as its effect the annulment of all existing differences and unites all existing things in a homogeneous mass at a single mathematical point. If two bodies exhibit a given difference and the difference has been annulled, the bodies can remain in a state of rest if the forces which were communicated to them for the purpose of removing the difference were to cease to exist. If these forces, however, are assumed to be indestructible and to continue in operation, still treated as causes of the change of state, they would then re-establish the originally existing difference. Therefore, the fundamental principle that forces once given are, like matter itself, quantitatively invariable, assures us conceptually of the continuance of existing differences and thereby the continued existence of the material world. We shall accordingly assume that science, which concerns itself with the nature of the existence of matter (chemistry) as well as with the nature of the existence of forces (physics), has to consider the *quantity* of its objects as the invariable thing and only the *quality* of these objects as variable.

The material objects *A* and *B*, whose relation to each other the forces strive to change, present the following relations: (1) They are either spatially separated, in which case the change in their relation is motion, or (2) they are not spatially separated and then changes in their relation refer to chemical reactions and to special types of relations arising from the contact of the substances and leading to electrical phenomena. Initially we shall restrict our attention to the type of force associated with change in spatial relations, that is, force that produces motion.

Let us assume we have two bodies which are isolated in the universe. If they are spatially separated from each other and allowed to move they will move toward each other in a straight line. The final cause of the forces, or the cause which manifests itself through the annulment of the difference between the bodies, communicates moving force *(bewegende Kraft)* to the bodies. As a consequence of this we see the motion take place. We represent quantitatively the motion existing at a given instant by the product of mass and velocity. Since causes are always related to each other in the same proportion as their effects, the moving forces are to each other as the resulting motions. Accordingly the product MC determines the moving force V. [Here M represents the mass and C the velocity of the body in question. Note that Mayer is here using momentum as the measure of force—Ed. note.] We set $V = MC$. If now we have a definite quantity of force $V = MC$, and hence a certain amount of motion results, the question arises as to the determination of how this quantity of force manifests itself or how the motion takes place. We conceptualize this under the name *quality* of motion. This includes within itself: (1) The energy *(energie)* of the motion or the relation between the intensity and extensity of the motion. [The use of the word *energie* here is mysterious. It has little relevance to modern terminology—Ed. note.] Controlling the latter is the number n in the expression $M/n\, nC$, where n can be any rational number, including an integer [It is difficult to understand Mayer here. However, he may think of M/n as representing the extensity of the motion and nC as representing the intensity. The product of the extensity and the intensity gives the whole quantity of motion—Ed. note.] The quality of motion also includes (2) the direction of the motion. In so far as it is a question of oppositely directed motion in the same straight line, this direction can be completely expressed by mere plus and minus signs. If this is not the case it is necessary to use the projection by lines whose length measures the quantity of motion. Let A and B be two bodies which are originally at a distance from each other and to which the moving forces v and v' are applied (gravitation being neglected). Let c and c' be their respective velocities, so that $v = Ac$ and $v' = Bc'$. In this way the quantities of motion are definitely determined [Mayer evidently intends that the quantity A measures the mass of body A, etc—Ed. note.] If $A = B$ and $v = v'$, the total quantity of moving force is $Q = 2Ac$ (since $c = c'$ also). For the determination of the quality of $2Ac$ we at first take the simplest case in which A and B move toward each other along the same straight line. Then $Ac = -Bc$. The sign for the united bodies A and B will be neither plus nor minus but zero, since A and B combined will not possess any motion either on one side or the other. The motion $2Ac$ must accordingly take place in such a way that every plus motion corresponds to an equal and opposite (negative) motion. Hence $2Ac$ can be neither plus nor minus but must itself have the sign zero. It is therefore clear what we are to understand by the expression $02Ac$. It is evident this is in no way actually equal to zero, and that the force quantity $2Ac$ loses nothing of its magnitude from the qualitative sign prefixed to it. [This bizarre notation indicates that Mayer had forgotten most of his mathematics. In particular at this time he had no grasp of vector analysis. Moreover, on the side of physics, he was, of course, handicapped by restricting himself to *momentum*, which is conserved in collisions, and ignoring *vis viva*, which is not in general conserved in collisions—Ed. note.] The measure of the differentiation from zero is given by $2Ac$. [For elastic collisions of the kind contemplated here, $2Ac$ is the magnitude of the change in momentum experienced by A as a result of the collision with B. Similarly for $2Bc$. It is understood, of course, that here $A = B$—Ed. note.] For a realization of $02Ac$, two oppositely directed motions are sufficient. Motions can take place in many directions. It is necessary only that to each motion there should correspond an equal motion in the opposite direction. From the point where A and B meet, radial oscillating or wave like motions can take place, as from a center. The further qualitative determination of the motion, that is the energy of the motion, rests in the determination of the number n in $02A/n\ nc$. The size of n depends on the physical condition of the bodies in question and their surroundings, and above all on the conductivity of the substances for the moving force, that is, the elasticity. If A and B are completely elastic, $n = 1$, and $+Ac$ will go into $-Ac$ (on collision) and $-Bc$ into $+Bc$ and conversely [It seems that here Mayer was thinking of the Newtonian coefficient of restitution in the collision of bodies. For perfectly elastic bodies, this coefficient is equal to unity, and the two objects of equal mass and equal speeds in the opposite direction rebound with the same speeds in the opposite direction—Ed. note.] As the measure of the elasticity decreases we see less motion developing and with complete absence of elasticity motion wholly ceases [Mayer here is referring to the collision of plastic balls along the same straight line going in opposite direction. They stick together and come to rest—Ed. note.] A part or all of the moving force will under such circumstances completely disappear from observation. [Mayer again confuses momentum with *vis viva*. Actually the momentum as a vector quantity is conserved in the example he cites. It is the *vis viva* or kinetic energy that is lost in part or in whole—Ed. note.] This part consisting of plus and minus we say has been neutralized. From the assumption of the invariability of quantity of force it follows that the neutralized motion is equal to the original motion minus the part that is left over. For complete inelasticity of A and B the neutralized motion $= 2Ac$. If now we represent the motion of A by ac and that of B by the equal and opposite bc (see the figure) it follows that $ab = 2Ac$

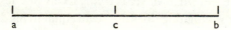

is the measure of the neutralized motion. The point c, which we call the mid-point, lies midway between a and b in the case for which motions of equal magnitude are oppositely directed. However, the null point, in so far as it can be considered a fixed point, can be placed at the end of the line. If a motion is made to cease at the fixed point b [Presumably by collision at a plastic wall—Ed. note.] once again we have $ab = 2Ac$ as the measure of the neutralized motion. The result is accordingly the same in both cases.

The motions ac and bc can neutralize each other completely [Mayer is still thinking of motions of the same momentum magnitude but opposite in direction and plastic collision—Ed. note.] if the angle $acb = 2$ right angles. This result will be incompletely realized if the angle acb is less than two right angles. If the angle $acb =$ zero, the motion continues with its full magnitude. In this case the neutralized motion is zero. If two motions combine while meeting at an angle the parallelogram of forces gives the resultant motion in magnitude and direction. The neutralization, as has been shown above, will then be equal to the motion originally present minus that left over. It is accordingly equal to the sum of the combined motions [Presumably sum of magnitudes only—Ed. note.] minus the resultant. It should be understood that the appearance of neutralization assumes the existence of real motion. In the case of statics there is no neutralization.

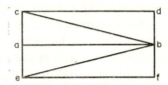

In the figure the rectangle $abdc$ represents two motions ab and ac which combine. If we take ad as positive, then $ab+ac = ad$ plus the neutralized motion N. Similarly $ab+ac = af$ plus the neutralized motion N. [One sees what Mayer is trying to say physically here, but his grasp of vector summation does not seem equal to his desire to provide a mathematical description of his intuitive feeling—Ed. note.] Since $ae = -ac$, it follows that $ab-ac = af$ plus N'. By $ab-ac$ we understand that to the motion ab another motion of magnitude ac but opposite in direction is added. Looked at in this way the combinations $ab+ac$ and $ab-ac$ give the same sum. In addition $ad+N = af+N'$. If on the other hand we wanted instead of adding the motion ae to ab to take away from it the equally great but oppositely directed motion *ac*, obviously the remainder would turn out to be smaller by 2*ac* (or *ce*) or 02*ac* than the earlier sum. If one wants to make this difference equal to zero, by the subtraction of *ac* and the addition of *ae* one gets the same result. The same holds for $ad - ac = ab + N'$. Without introducing further examples we call attention briefly to the fact that in the usual application of the parallelogram (of forces or motions) principle in dynamics we always get results leading to a neutralized motion either too small or too large; otherwise, however, they are completely correct so far as the nature of real motion is concerned. The differences with respect to the neutralized motions become zero in the calculation if, as the case demands, we let oppositely directed motions become zero, or derive from zero what we need in the way of oppositely direction motions. Since forces can evade observation in our physical apparatus, but can never be produced out of nothing, those cases are appropriate for experimentation in which a neutralized motion is neglected or discarded. But those cases are inappropriate in which the production of such a motion is assumed to take place out of nothing. Accordingly we may be successful in compounding *ab* and *ac* to get the sum *ad*, but never be able to resolve *ad* into two motions unambiguously, since the directions of the components can be arbitrary.

We are now permitted to draw from the foregoing some conclusions about natural science. The neutralized motion 02*MC*, in so far as the motion does not take place in opposite directions, is the expression for heat. Motion, heat, and as we intend to show later, electricity are phenomena which can be attributed to a single force and can be transformed into each other in accordance with definite laws. Motion is transformed into heat by virtue of being neutralized by an opposite motion or by a fixed point [Mayer evidently is thinking here of collision with a rigid wall coated with a plastic substance—Ed. note.] The heat produced is proportional to the motion that disappears. Heat, on the other hand, is transformed into motion by means of expanding bodies. In accordance with the formula 02*MC* (or $+ MC - MC$) it brings about opposite motions in all directions (radially) whereas the heated body itself remains at rest. This is why the qualitative symbol zero (0) is attached to it. Waves and oscillating motions form a special class with respect to the transformation of simple motion to heat. In so far as they are radial they have the symbol zero (0) attached to them. These motions are distinguished from heat by the fact that they continue to maintain themselves as motion as time goes on and the quantity of this motion is always represented by $2MC$. In accordance with the different forms of energy they lead to different phenomena. In the formula $M/n \cdot nC$, the number n represents the energy of the motion. When n is very large, or as we may say for brevity equal to infinity, we get the kind of motion corresponding to light or radiant heat. We may apply the formula $02M/\infty \propto C$ to light. From light we get heat if the motion becomes rest. From heat we get light, if the accumulated neutralized motion takes the form of actual motion.

If we join a body P to a fixed point c by an ideal radius vector and give to P a central motion MC, this motion is resolved into two motions. The one is in the direction of the periphery. The other lies along the direction Pc. The latter is continually neutralized by the fixed point. From this we see that the motion MC communicated to P gradually becomes $0MC$ at c. Accordingly the motion of P is a gradually decreasing one. In the system of the heavenly bodies gravitation takes the place of the ideal, artificial radius vector above. Instead of having a motion in the direction $-Pc$ taken away from the motion MC, a motion $+Pc$ is communicated to MC and through the combined moving forces in accordance with the principles of status and dynamics the continuous revolution of the heavenly bodies is not only achieved, but also in every revolution a definite amount of motion is neutralized in c. In other words the center falls toward the periphery to the same extent as P falls toward the center. In the systems of the stars, the problem, unsolvable by us, of providing a continuous source of force, that is, the change from 0 to $+MC-MC$, is solved by Nature. The fruit of this is the most magnificent of the material world: the eternal source of light [*Note by Mayer:* The author has presented the foregoing principles, forming in part his view of nature, in the briefest possible form. Truth needs few words for its recognition, and to try to praise error as truth is a vain struggle].

On the Forces of Inorganic Nature

Editorial Preface

This is the first paper of Mayer to be published. It appeared in Liebig's *Annalen der Chemie und Pharmacie* (vol. 42, p. 233, 1842). It was republished in *Gesammelte Schriften und Briefe von Robert Mayer*, Jacob J. Weyrauch, 2 vols, Stuttgart, Cotta, 1893 (Vol. 1, *Die Mechanik der Wärme*). It was later reprinted in Ostwald's *Klassiker der Exakten Wissenschaften*, No. 180, with the title page *Die Mechanik der Wärme, Zwei Abhandlungen von Robert Mayer, herausgegeben von A. von Oettingen*, Leipzig, Verlag von Wilhelm Engelmann, 1911, p. 1.

The following translation is that of the author of this book and is based on the version appearing in Ostwald's *Klassiker*. Another translation was made by J. C. Foster and appeared in *Phil. Mag.* (4th series), vol. 24, 1862. This was reprinted in *The Correlation and Conservation of Forces*, an anthology edited by E. L. Youmans, D. Appleton and Company, New York, 1886, p. 251.

The interpolated editorial notes by the present translator are intended to clarify some parts of Mayer's presentation from the standpoint of modern ideas. A more complete critique of the paper is found in Part II.

THE purpose of the following article is to seek for an answer to the question: what are we to understand by *forces* (Kräfte) and how are these related to each other? Through the name *matter* we attribute to objects definite properties such as weight and volume. To the name *force* (Kraft) on the other hand there is joined the idea of the unknown, the inscrutable, the hypothetical. An attempt to make the idea of *force* as precise as that of *matter* and to denote thereby only objects of real inquiry, together with the attempt to understand the consequences flowing from this, might not be unwelcome to friends of a clear, hypothesis-free view of Nature.

Forces are causes. To them there is immediate application of the fundamental principle: *Causa aequat effectum* (the cause equals the effect). If the cause c has the effect e, then $c = e$. If e is in turn the cause of another effect f, $e = f$ and so on: $c = e = f = \ldots = e$. As is clear from the nature of an equation, in a causal chain of this kind, no member nor a part of a member can ever be zero. This property of all causes we call its indestructibility.

If a given cause c has brought about its equal effect e, then c has ceased to exist: c has become e. If after the production of e, the whole or part of c were left over, the part remaining could be the cause of other effects. The total effect of c would therefore exceed e which would contradict the hypothesis $c = e$. Since c is transformed into e, e into f, etc., it follows that we must consider these quantities as different manifestations of one and the same object. The ability to assume different forms is the second essential characteristic of all causes. In summarizing both properties, we say: causes are quantitatively indestructible and qualitatively transformable objects.

In Nature we find two classes of causes between which we learn from experience no transitions take place. The one class is made up of those causes which have the properties of ponderability (weight) and inpenetrability, namely what we commonly call *matter*. The other is made up of those causes which do not possess these properties—these are the forces, which from the designated negative properties are also called *imponderables*. Accordingly forces are indestructible, transformable and imponderable entities.

A cause which brings about the raising of a weight is a force. Its effect, the raised weight, is accordingly likewise a force. Expressed in more general terms this means that the spatial separation of ponderable objects is a force. Since this force brings about the fall of the object, we call it a *fall-force* (Fallkraft), or the force connected with falling. Fall-force and fall, or more generally fall-force and motion are forces which are related to each other as cause and effect. They are forces which can be transformed, one into another; they are two different manifestations, of the same entity. For example, a weight resting on the ground is no force; it is neither the cause of a motion nor the cause of the raising of another weight. It becomes such a cause, however, to the extent to which it is raised above the ground. The cause, the displacement of the weight from the earth and the effect, the amount of motion which is produced, stand in a constant relation to each other, as mechanics shows.

If in considering gravity as the cause of the fall of an object we speak of the force of gravity we confuse the concepts of force and property. Every property must dispense with precisely that which is attached to every force, namely the union of indestructibility and transformability. Between a property and a force (e.g., between gravity and motion) we cannot therefore set up the necessary equation for a correct causal relation: If we call gravity a force we have to think of it as a cause which produces an effect without itself decreasing in magnitude. It therefore involves an incorrect representation of the causal connection of things. In order that a body should be able to fall its elevation from the ground is no less necessary then its weight (gravity). One may not therefore ascribe the falling of the body to gravity alone.

It is the object of mechanics to develop the equations which exist between fall-force and motion, between motion and fall-force and between motions in general. Here we recall only one point. The magnitude of the fall-force (if we take the earth's radius as effectively infinite) is directly proportional to the mass m and the displacement d above the ground. That is, $v = md$. [In modern terminology if m is really the mass of the falling particle, we should write $v = gmd$, where g is the acceleration of gravity. It seems clear that Mayer used mass and weight interchangeably. If his m is weight, his formula is correct. In any case his fall-force v corresponds to potential energy for the case of free fall, in modern terminology—Ed. note.] Suppose with $d = 1$, the final velocity of the mass on reaching the ground is $c = 1$, then we can also express v as equal to mc. In general, however, $v = mc^2$ is the measure of the fall-force. The law of the conservation of *vis visa* is based on the general law of the indestructibility of causes. [Mayer seems to be saying here that we use the product of mass and velocity (mc) as a measure of fall-force only if the velocity c gained by a fall from height d were equal to unity for $d = 1$. He recognizes that $v = mc^2$ is a more valid representation for fall force, with $c = \sqrt{2gd}$, etc. He fails to stress the point that v cannot be measured by both momentum and *vis viva* since they are different dimensionally. Incidentally Mayer consistently uses *vis viva* in place of $mc^2/2$, the modern kinetic energy. He was still following Leibniz—Ed. note.]

In countless cases we see a motion cease without bringing about another motion or the raising of a weight. However, a force once in existence cannot become zero, but must reappear in another form. The question then arises: what other form can be taken on by the force which we designate as fall-force or motion? Experience alone can provide information on this point. In order to experiment profitably in this matter, we must choose instruments which while causing the motion to cease, are themselves changed but little by the objects under investigation. For example, if we rub two metal plates together, we make motion disappear and on the other hand observe the production of heat. The question then arises: is the motion the cause of the heat? In order to be sure about this relation, we must discuss the further question: in the countless cases in which the appearance of heat has been detected on the cessation of motion, has not the motion had some other effect than the appearance of heat and has not the heat another cause than the cessation of motion?

An attempt to demonstrate the results of the cessation of motion has never been seriously carried out. [Mayer was at this time presumably ignorant of the work J. P. Joule had been doing in England as well as that of Colding in Denmark—Ed. note.] Without desiring to dismiss in *a priori* fashion the possible hypothesis that may be set up, we yet call attention to the fact that the effect cannot in general be associated with a change in the state of aggregation of the bodies that are moved and rubbed together, etc. If we assume that a certain quantity of motion v is expended in the transformation of a rubbed material m into n, then $m+v = n$ or $n = m+v$. By the transformation of n back into m, v must reappear in some form. In the very long continued rubbing of two metal plates we can cause repeatedly the cessation of an enormous amount of motion. Can we really expect to find in the metal dust a trace of the force that has disappeared? We repeat that the motion cannot be reduced to *nothing*. Oppositely directed or positive and negative motions cannot become zero any more than oppositely directed motions can arise from nothing or a weight rise by itself alone.

No account can be given of the disappearance of motion without the recognition of a causal connection between motion and heat, any more than we can explain the existence of frictional heat without this same recognition. The production of frictional heat cannot be explained by the decrease in the volume of the bodies being rubbed together. It is well known that one can melt two pieces of ice by rubbing them together in a vacuum, but let anyone try to melt ice by the mere increase in pressure on it. [Some years after the publication of this paper, Sir William Thomson (later Lord Kelvin) showed that the melting point of ice is lowered by the application of pressure. The thermodynamic problem involved is more complicated than Mayer or his contemporaries could have visualized. In any case Kelvin's result applies only to substances which expand on freezing (like ice). For substances which contract on freezing (like bismuth) the effect of pressure is to *raise* the melting point—Ed. note.] Water when shaken violently experiences a rise in temperature as the author found. The heated water (at around 12 °C or 13 °C) experiences an increase in volume. Whence then comes the heat which can be produced in arbitrary amounts by repeated shaking of the water in the same apparatus? The thermal vibration hypothesis leans toward the principle that heat is the effect of motion but does not accept this causal connection at its full value, putting the principal stress on the vibrations themselves.

If it now develops that in many cases no other effect can be found for the vanishing motions save heat *(exceptio confirmat regulam)* [This is a rather strange interpolation. The Latin statement is usually put in the form: *exceptio probat regulam* (The exception tests the rule). Mayer's form may have meant to him that the exception calls attention to the necessity of investigating the rule more carefully!—Ed. note.] and for the heat that appears no other cause can be found than the motion, we prefer the assumption that heat originates from motion to the assumption of a cause without an effect or an effect without a cause, just as the chemist, instead of allowing the disappearance of hydrogen and oxygen and the appearance of water to go without inquiry, postulates a connection between hydrogen and oxygen on the one hand and water on the other.

We can visualize the naturally existing connection between fall-force, motion and heat in the following fashion. We know that heat makes its appearance if the individual particles of a body move closer together; compression produces heat. That which holds for the smallest particles and the smallest spaces separating them must clearly find an application to large masses and measurable spaces. The falling of a weight is a real decrease in the volume of the earth and must therefore stand in some relation to the heat produced. This heat must be exactly proportional to the magnitude of the weight and its original distance from the earth's surface. From this consideration we are led very simply to the relation connecting fall-force, heat and motion as mentioned above.

From the relation connecting fall-force and motion we have no right to draw the conclusion that the essential nature of fall-force *is* motion, nor have we any greater right to draw this conclusion for heat. We should rather take the opposite view that in order to become heat, motion (whether it be simple motion or vibrating motion like light or radiant heat) must cease to be motion.

If fall-force and motion are equivalent to heat, naturally heat must be equivalent to fall-force and motion. Just as heat results as an effect of volume decrease and the cessation of motion, so heat disappears as a cause on the appearance of its effects: motion, volume expansion, elevation of a weight.

In the mills operated by water wheels the motion that is produced and again disappears, resulting indeed from the volume decrease which the earth continually suffers through the fall of the water, produces in turn a significant quantity of heat. Conversely the steam engine serves to transform heat into motion and the raising of weights. The steam locomotive and its accompanying train may be compared to a distillation apparatus; the heat produced in the boiler is transformed into motion, which in turn is changed back into heat (at least in part) in the wheel axles.

We complete our thesis, which necessarily follows from the fundamental principle: *causa aequat effectum* and which stands in complete accord with all natural phenomena, with a practical conclusion. For the solution of the equations connecting fall-force and motion, magnitude of the fall must be determined by experiment for a definite period of time, e.g., for the first second of fall. Similarly, for the solution of the equation existing between fall-force and motion, on the one hand and heat on the other, we must ask ourselves the question: how great is the quantity of heat corresponding to a definite amount of fall-force and motion? For example, we must discover how high a definite weight must be raised above the surface of the earth in order that its fall-force shall be equivalent to the heating of an equal weight of water from 0 °C to 1 °C. That such a relation actually exists in nature can serve as the resumé of the considerations presented in this essay.

By the application of the principles developed here to the heat and volume relations of a gas, we find the decrease in height of a mercury column compressing a gas equivalent to the quantity of heat associated with the compression. If we put the ratio of the specific heat capacities of the gas at constant pressure and constant volume respectively equal to 1.421, it turns out that the fall of a weight from a height of about 365 meters corresponds to the heating of an equal mass of water from 0 °C to 1 °C. Comparing with this result the efficiency of our best steam engines, we see what a small part of the heat transferred to the boiler is really transformed into motion or the raising of a weight. This could justify the attempt to produce motion in other ways than through the use of the chemical reaction between carbon and oxygen. This might be by the transformation of the electricity obtained chemically directly into motion in an efficient fashion.

The Motions of Organisms and their Relation to Metabolism. An Essay in Natural Science

Editorial Preface

This was the second scientific paper of Mayer to be published. With the German title "Die organische Bewegung in ihiem Zusammenhang mit dem Stoffwechsel. Ein Beitrag zur Naturkunde" it was brought out by Verlag der C. Drechslerschen Buchhandlung in Heilbronn in 1845. It was republished in *Gesammelte Schriften und Briefe von Robert Mayer*, Jacob J. Weyrauch, 2 Vols, Stuttgart, Cotta, 1893 (Vol. 1, *Die Mechanik der Wärme*). It was later reprinted in Ostwald's *Klassiker der Exakten Naturwissenschaften*, No. 180, with the title page *Die Mechanik der Wärme*, Zwei Abhandlungen von Robert Mayer, herausgegeben von A. von Oettingen, Leipzig, Verlag von Wilhelm Engelmann, 1911, p. 9.

The following translation is by the author of this book and is based on the version appearing in Ostwald's *Klassiker*. The interpolated editorial notes by the translator are intended to clarify some parts of Mayer's presentation from the standpoint of modern ideas. A more complete critique is found in Part II.

Introduction

In the course of the last century applied mathematics has attained such a high stage of development and its conclusions have acquired such a high degree of certainty that it has been justified in assuming the first rank among the sciences. It is the beginning and the end for the astronomer, the technologist and the navigator, it is the solid axis of all the natural philosophy of the present time. It is only in biology that the discoveries of Galileo, Newton and Mariotte have borne comparatively little fruit. No formulas have been found for the phenomena of life, for the letter killeth, the spirit alone giveth life!

In the study of motions produced organically the gulf between mathematical physics and physiology, which even the outstanding investigations of people like Schwann and Valentin have not been able to bridge, is vividly perceptible. Therefore the attempt to set up a method by which both sciences can be brought closer together with reference to the matter in question should not be without interest to physiologists.

It must indeed be considered a relapse into the mistakes of ancient natural philosophy or the confusion of modern science if there were in view an attempt to construct a universe *a priori*. When, however, there has been success in tying together countless natural phenomena and from them to deduce a fundamental law of nature one should not be reproached if after careful tests one uses this law as a compass to guide his path with greater assurance over the sea of details.

Proceeding from the laws of inorganic phenomena we take for granted on the one hand the results of mechanics as established truths, while on the other hand we do not feel obliged to accept all the concepts and classifications which mechanics has found it good to set up as binding on our considerations. Mechanics, so to speak, anatomizes or dissects the natural objects with which it deals by abstractions pushed as far as possible until they correspond to numbers in its mathematical

76

analysis, and is content to be able to answer the questions which it raises with admirable sharpness and mathematical accuracy. Mechanics is troubled but little if through its way of looking at things phenomena which are closely associated in nature appear on the boundary of the mechanical domain to be widely separate. Mechanics is concerned just as little about the apparent coincidence, in its domain, of concepts and objects which in the real world have nothing in common.

The concepts which mechanics has constructed for its purposes have been pushed further by other sciences than mechanics itself could tolerate. Suppose the question arises, what is to be understood by a "body"? The geometer will answer: "Without prejudice to the physicist, zoologist, psychologist, etc., a body according to geometrical concepts is a space bounded in three dimensions." The expert in mechanics, who represents the origin, changes in and cessation of motion as brought about by a pressure calls this, *in abstracto*, "force" *(Kraft)*. The ability of a mass to exercise such a pressure, i.e., gravity or weight, he calls a force. However, without sticking to the abstraction force = pressure of the mechanist, other scientists have tended to treat weight as the general type of all forces and thereby have introduced an artificial confusion of the concepts: property, force, cause and effect. This has proved to be a serious handicap in the building of the tower of knowledge.

Before we begin an investigation of physiological laws we may be permitted to make intelligible the concept of force *(Kraft)* and to represent the important inorganic phenomena in their natural connections with one another.

In the composition of the inorganic part of this work the author has taken considerable trouble to set forth the relevant mechanical and physical problems in a generally intelligible way. Should nevertheless individual points arise for the understanding of which a more exact acquaintance with the theorems of mechanics is required, in the nature of the case these could not very well be avoided.

It is to be hoped that physicists for whom the calculus is a tool in their investigations and not an end in itself will not deny an earnest examination to this part of the author's work.

If a mass initially at rest is to be put in motion the expenditure of force is necessary. A motion never arises by itself: it arises from its *cause*, namely force.

Ex nihilo nil fit

We call force an entity which through its expenditure brings about motion. Force as a cause of motion is an indestructible entity. No effect arises without a cause. No cause disappears without a corresponding effect.

Ex nihilo nil fit. Nil fit ad nihilum

The effect is equal to the cause. The effect of force is once again force. The quantitative unchangeability (invariance) of the given is one of the fundamental laws of nature which applies equally to force and matter.

Chemistry teaches us to recognize the qualitative changes which given matter undergoes under different conditions. It provides in every individual case the proof that in chemical processes only the *form* and not the *magnitude* of the given matter is changed.*

What chemistry performs with respect to matter, physics has to perform in the case of force. The only mission of physics is to become acquainted with force in its various forms and to investigate the conditions governing its changes. The creation or destruction of a force, if they have any meaning, lies outside the domain of human thought and action.

Whether in the future it will prove possible to transmute the many chemical elements into one another, or to reduce them to a few simpler elements or even to a single fundamental substance, is more than doubtful. The same situation, however, does not hold for the causes of motion. It can be proved *a priori* and confirmed everywhere by experience that the various forms of forces *can* be transformed into one another.

---

* A piece of matter A suffers through the addition of another piece of matter B a change in size. Since B as well as A must be considered as given and the sum $A + B$ of their parts taken together is equal, it is clear that the given as a whole suffers no change in size by the composition or separation of the parts.

In truth there exists only a *single* force. In never-ending exchange this circles through all dead as well as living nature. In the latter as well as the former nothing happens without form variation of force! [For *force* here and throughout read *energy* in the modern notation. In the rest of the translation we make this change—Ed. note.]

1

Motion is a form of energy. In the enumeration of forms of energy it merits the first place. Heat warms, motion moves.

When a moving mass meets one at rest, the latter is set in motion whereas the first loses some motion. If in billiards the white ball collides squarely with the red one, the white one loses its velocity and the red one moves on with the velocity the white one has lost. It is the motion of the white ball which when expended brings about the motion of the red one or we may say is transformed into the latter. The motion of the white ball is a form of energy. The motion of the red one is an effect which is equal to cause; it is also a form of energy.

A billiard ball can by collision set many other balls in motion and still remain in motion itself. The magnitude of the *vis viva* (kinetic energy) of the whole system, however, stays the same before and after the collision.

2

A mass at rest at any arbitrary distance above the earth's surface and then released will immediately set itself in motion and will reach the ground with a velocity which is readily calculable. The motion of this mass cannot arise without the expenditure of energy. What is this latter energy?

If we restrict ourselves not to traditional assumptions but to the simple facts of experience, we readily become aware that it is the raising of the weight which is the cause of the motion of the weight. For example, a pound weight [500 grams as Mayer took it] was at rest 15 feet [1 foot = 32.484 centimeters in Mayer's units] above the ground. In falling freely to the ground, the final velocity is 30 feet per second [$v = \sqrt{2}\,gh$, etc.]. The raising of the weight was expended, but the motion of the weight was brought into existence.

Hence raising the weight is the cause of motion and is a form of energy. This energy causes the fall motion. We call it *Fall kraft* [fall energy or in modern terminology potential energy].

If a mass moves along a horizontal plane with a certain velocity it keeps this velocity constant due to the law of inertia, as we are accustomed to say. The same mass, however, with the same initial velocity, if it begins to move vertically upwards loses its motion completely in a few seconds. Suppose a mass of 1 pound starts to move up with a velocity of 30 feet per second. After 1 second the motion has ceased, and the 1 pound mass has been lifted to 15 feet above the ground. The energy which has raised this load is its motion; what was previously effect is now the cause, what was cause has now become effect. Fall energy has been transformed into motion and motion in turn transformed into fall energy.

The magnitude of the fall energy is measured by the product of weight and height (mgh, if g = acceleration of gravity). The magnitude of the motion as energy (motional energy) is given by one-half the product of the mass and the square of the velocity. [Here the author presents some mechanical formulas relating to motion of gravitating masses which are not included here—Ed. note.] Both forms of energy are represented by the collective name of mechanical effect.

If fall energy is transformed into motion or vice versa, the total mechanical effect maintains a constant value. This law, a special case of the axiom of the indestructibility of energy is known in mechanics as the principle of the conservation of *vis viva* [This is bad terminology, as in most cases the *vis viva* actually changes, even when the total mechanical energy = *vis viva* + potential energy stays constant—Ed. note.] As examples consider free fall from any height, fall along prescribed paths, pendulum oscillations, motions of the heavenly bodies.

3

For a thousand years or more, the human race was almost exclusively restricted to the ever-recurring problem of setting resting masses in motion by means of the tools of inorganic nature, in particular the application of given mechanical effects. It was reserved for a later time to add a new type of energy to the energy forms of the old world, i.e., those of streaming wind and flowing water. This third form of energy which our century gazes on with wonder is *heat*.

Heat is a form of energy. It can be transformed into mechanical energy.*

Let us suppose that a wagon train having a mass of 100,000 pounds is given a velocity of 30 feet per second. By the expenditure of an appropriate amount of energy this can be achieved. For example, the wagon train can gain this velocity by rolling down a suitable inclined plane. As a rule, however, the train will be set in motion without the expenditure of "fall energy" (potential energy) and in spite of friction, etc., will maintain this motion. When a rise in elevation of the path of 1 part in 150 is assumed (as equivalent to the friction) then a velocity of 30 feet per second will be enough to raise the train load 720 feet high in 1 hour, which corresponds to an expenditure of 45 horsepower. This enormous quantity of motion originally produced assumes an equally great quantity of expended energy of some kind. The effective energy in the case of a locomotive pulling a train is *heat*.

The expenditure of heat or the transformation of heat into motion rests on the fact that the quantity of heat which is taken up by the steam is continually greater than that which is given up when the steam is exhausted and condensed in the surroundings. The difference is the heat transformed into mechanical activity (work).

Equal quantities of combustible material under the same conditions give equal quantities of heat. However, the coal burned under the boiler provides less free heat when the engine is working then when it is not. The free heat distributes itself to the surroundings and hence is lost for mechanical purposes. The more perfect (efficient?) the apparatus, by

---

* If here a transformation of heat into mechanical effects is laid down as something that takes place it is stated only as a fact, and in no way is the thing given an explanation. Thus a given amount of ice is transformed into a corresponding amount of water: This fact is simply so and remains independent of the unfruitful speculations on how and why. Real science remains satisfied with positive knowledge and freely leaves to poets and philosophers the solution of such everlasting riddles with the help of fantasy.

so much the less will heat be transferred to the surroundings. The best engines give an efficiency of about 5 per cent. One hundred pounds of hard coal in such an engine provide no greater quantity of free heat than 95 pounds of coal, burning without doing any work.

For the establishment of this important law we must examine the behavior of elastic fluids with respect to heat and mechanical action.

Gay-Lussac has proved by experiment that an elastic fluid (gas) which streams out of a vessel into an equally large evacuated container suffers in the former vessel just as much cooling as the latter vessel warms up. This investigation of outstanding simplicity, which has been confirmed by other observers, shows that a given weight and volume of an elastic fluid can expand two-fold, four-fold or to a volume of any size without experiencing *on the whole* any temperature change. This means that for the expansion of the gas in and for itself no heat expenditure is necessary. At the same time experiment confirms that when a gas expands against pressure it suffers a drop in temperature.

Let us assume that 1 cubic inch of air at 0 °C and a pressure of 27 inches of mercury [standard conditions] is heated by a quantity of heat x at constant volume to 274 °C. When this gas is allowed to expand into an evacuated space of the same volume it will still retain the temperature 274 °C and a medium surrounding the vessels containing the gas will during the expansion experience no change in temperature. Now, however, consider the other case in which 1 cubic inch of air is heated from 0 °C to 274 °C not at constant volume but at constant pressure (namely 27 inches of mercury). In this case a larger quantity of heat is required. Represent this as $x+y$.

In both cases above the air is heated from 0 °C to 274° and in both cases the air expanded from one volume to twice the volume.

In the first case the quantity of heat required was x. In the second it was $x+y$. In the first case the mechanical effect produced was zero, but in the second it was the equivalent of raising 15 pounds 1 inch.

If the air is cooled under the same circumstances under which it was heated, an amount of heat is given back equal to that which was taken up. The given amount of air if it is cooled from 274 °C to 0 °C without the simultaneous expenditure of mechanical work (or with pressure absent) will accordingly give back the quantity of heat $= x$. However, in cooling under constant pressure with the expenditure of potential energy equivalent to that needed to raise 15 pounds 1 inch, the air will give back the quantity of heat $x + y$.

The steam in the engine when it expands behaves like the air at constant pressure. The quantity of heat needed for the heating and expansion of the steam is $x + y$. In the cooling process the steam experiences no particular pressure and hence the cooling takes place without (or with very small) expenditure of mechanical work. It gives back the heat quantity x. Hence there is associated with every cycle of the piston in the cylinder of the engine a heat loss equal to y. Thus the operation of the engine is inseparately connected with a consumption of heat.*

The quantity of heat which must be expended to produce a definite amount of mechanical work must be evaluated experimentally.

The total expenditure of heat can be calculated from the quantity of combustible material burned in the engine. When the inevitable losses of heat through radiation, conduction and convection are deducted from the above, there remains the heat really available for transformation and this corresponds to the actual performance of the engine. Since, however, by far the greater part of the unused and dissipated heat can be only approximately estimated, even a partially reliable result is hardly to be expected along these lines.

The problem can be solved more simply and precisely by calculation of the quantity of heat which becomes latent† if a gas expands under pressure. If the heat taken up by the gas in heating it by t °C at

---

* The periodic rise and fall of the engine beam would in and of itself not bring about a continuous expenditure of energy or a consumption of heat. Once set in motion the balance beam of the engine would move by itself [barring friction, etc.]. Like a pendulum in vibration it moves without net energy expenditure.

† The concepts of heat becoming latent and free are equivalent to those of expenditure and production respectively. We can say that motion becomes *latent* when an object moves up from the earth and the motion slows down. It becomes free when the motion is downward. Heat may be thought of as latent motion, just as motion may be thought of as latent heat.

constant volume is x, the heat needed to heat the gas through the same temperature range at constant pressure will be $x+y$. If in the latter case the weight raised is P, then $y = Ph$.

One cubic centimeter of atmospheric air at 0 °C and 0.76 meters barometric pressure weighs (has a mass of) 0.0013 gram. If it is heated through 1 °C the air expands by 1/274 part of its volume and at the same time raises a column of mercury of 1 square centimeter cross-section and 76 centimeters high by 1/274 meter. The weight of this column is 1033 grams. The specific heat of air (that of water taken as unity), from the work of Delaroche and Berard, is 0.267. The quantity of heat which a cubic centimeter of air takes up in order to go from 0 °C to 1 °C at constant pressure is accordingly equal to the heat by which $(0.0013)(0.267) = 0.000347$ gram of water would have its temperature raised by 1 °C. According to Dulong, whom most physicists follow, the quantity of heat which air takes up to heat itself by 1 °C at constant volume to that for constant pressure is in the ratio 1 : 1.421. If we use this we calculate the heat needed to heat 1 cubic centimeter of air by 1 °C at constant volume as $0.00037/1.421 = 0.000244$. [There is an obvious misprint here. Mayer has 1.41 in place of 1.421. His result, however, agrees with the choice of 1.421. Ironically 1.41 is in better agreement with modern values of the ratio of the specific heats—Ed. note.]

The difference $(x+y)-x = y$ is therefore $0.000347-0.000244 = 0.000103$ units of heat [Mayer uses degree (°) of heat. Actually he is using equivalent calories—Ed. note.] By the expenditure of this, 1033 grams of mercury is lifted 1/274 centimeters. Hence 1 unit of heat [1 calorie] is equivalent to 1 gram raised 367 meters [or an energy of 3.59 joules—Ed. note.]*

The same result will be obtained if in place of atmospheric air one

---

* Mayer inserts a footnote, evidently added in the second edition of his paper, that a more accurate experimental value of the ratio of the specific heat provides a value of the mechanical equivalent more nearly in agreement with Joule's value. He says he wants to leave his original value in the main text, though in subsequent applications, in the revised version of his paper, he uses effectively 4.165 joules per calorie (though not in these units, of course).

takes and applies a similar calculation to any other simple or complex gas.*

The law: "heat equals mechanical energy" is independent of the nature of the elastic fluid in question. The latter acts only as a vehicle for the transformation of the one form of energy into the other. Among the differing (but not too widely separated) data on the heats of combustion of carbon, those of Liebig are probably most reliable. From the direct experimental observations of Dulong which were published by Arago after Dulong's death, Liebig calculated that the quantity of heat developed in the burning of 1 gram of carbon to CO_2 is 8558 calories. [Mayer does not use the term calorie, but this is what he means—Ed. note.] (*Annalen der Chemie von Wöhler und Liebig*, vol. 53, p. 73).

In the combustion of 1 gram of carbon, therefore, work equivalent to the raising of 3.6×10^6 grams of carbon though 1 meter is involved. This result would be achieved if all heat losses were avoided. But we have no more chance of changing a given amount of heat *all* into work in one operation than we have of transforming chlorine, hydrogen

---

* In other words this means: if the heat capacity of atmospheric air under constant pressure is taken to be equal to *unity*, and if the heat capacity of any other gas under constant pressure is S, and if K is the ratio of the specific heats for this other gas, under the assumption of the same coefficient of expansion [all ideal gases], we must have

$$S\left(\frac{K-1}{K}\right) = \frac{0.421}{1.421}$$

[which is clearly satisfied for $K = 1.421$ and $S = 1$]. This result agrees with the experimental work of Dulong. For CO_2 he gets $S = 1.175$ and $K = 1.388$, so that we should have

$$(1.175)\frac{(0.338)}{1.338} = \frac{0.421}{1.421}$$

and we do. Similarly for olefiant gas Dulong has $S = 1.531$ and $K = 1.240$, so that

$$(1.531)\frac{(0.240)}{1.240} = \frac{0.421}{1.421}$$

checking again. Also Dulong's famous law that all elastic fluids when they are compressed by the same fractional change in volume liberate the same amounts of heat is one of the necessary consequences of the general law: Heat equals mechanical work.

and a metal into a metallic chloride salt without the formation of other products.

It is a technological problem to minimize as much as possible the unwanted effect of combustion, that is the liberation of heat into space (without doing useful work). In the first engines of Watt, according to John Taylor, the quantity of coal burned for a given amount of work done was seventeen times greater than in the engines developed in 1828.

At that time even under the most favorable circumstances engines working with 1 pound of anthracite could lift about a half million pounds 1 foot. While the maximum efficiency attainable was about 5 to 6 per cent, many engines, locomotives in particular, scarcely reached an efficiency of 1 per cent.

Guns achieve a better performance. Let us figure that a 24 pound shot can be given a muzzle velocity of 1500 feet per second by means of the burning of 8 pounds of powder containing 1 pound of carbon. In this case the mechanical efficiency attains a value of 9 per cent. However, it is well known that a gun loaded with ball is heated less with the same charge of powder then the same gun firing a blank.

If we assume that the whole earth's crust could be raised on suitably placed pillars around its surface, the raising of this immeasurable load would require the transformation of an enormous amount of heat.

Since it is clear that such a volume increase in the earth is connected with a corresponding quantity of heat becoming "latent", it is likewise clear that in a volume decrease of the earth a corresponding quantity of heat will be set free. But whatever holds for the earth's crust as a whole must also apply to every fraction thereof. In the raising of the smallest weight, heat (or some equivalent form of energy) must become latent; and by the falling of this weight to the earth's surface, the same quantity of heat must be set free.

It has already been seen that in the raising of 1 kilogram through 425 meters, a unit of heat is necessary. This is equivalent to saying that the raising of one gram through the same height demands 1 calorie of heat. We can also say that a kilogram which drops through 425 meters through collision or friction must develop 1 large calorie of heat (1000 ordinary calories). [Mayer's notation here has been converted into the modern form. He is not always careful to dinstinguish between the ordinary calorie and the kilogram calorie—Ed. note.]

Physicists were prevented by their traditional presuppositions on the energy of motion and motion itself from grasping the above evident fact which is fully confirmed by experience. Newton in his *Principia* (Definition VIII) states expressly that gravity is a *causa mathematica* (mathematical cause) and cautions against treating it as a *causa physica* (physical cause)*. This important distinction was, however, neglected by Newton's successors. Gravity or the cause of acceleration was taken as the cause of motion itself, and thereby the occurrence of motion without expenditure of energy was ordained, in so far as in the falling of a weight, no gravity was expended. As a necessary consequence of its method of origin given motion was allowed under certain circumstances to eventually become nothing.[†] [Mayer is continually disturbed by the current use of gravity as a force. It is a force in the Newtonian sense, but not in Mayer's sense (i.e. as energy)—Ed. note.]

We find here accordingly two contradictory points of view. Either a given motion by its disappearance is supposed to go to zero, or it will have an indestructible effect equal to itself. If we unconditionally decide for the latter we are appealing to the laws of thought as well as to experience.

If we draw from a reservoir, a lake or even from the ocean a glass of water, we will not be able to detect the corresponding decrease in the large amount of water in question. If, however, one is willing to grant that these bodies of water have actually suffered no loss of substance at all by the withdrawal of a few ounces of water, then necessarily the

---

* The *causa mathematica* of Newton, in particular the force of gravity, is the cause or measure of acceleration. If v is the force and c the velocity, then $v = dc/dt$ [He leaves out m; strictly $v = mdc/dt$ — Ed. note]. But in the use of force in the energy sense, the *causa physica* is the measure of motion. If the *Kraft* [he means energy] is v, we have $v = mc^2$ [Strictly kinetic energy $\frac{1}{2}mc^2$ — Ed. note].

† The mathematical expression for this second paradox is the so-called Cartesian measure of force, namely quantity of motion or momentum.

conclusion follows that these ounces have been created out of nothing and when given back to the sea revert to nothing.

The same conclusion holds for the forces. We accordingly ask: is the "moving force" which gives a weight falling to the earth from a position 30 feet above its surface a velocity of 30 feet per second, a constant? People are accustomed to answer this as follows: the increase and decrease in gravitational force over such a small distance may be completely neglected and hence "Yes" is the answer to the question. We say "No". If the force were constant, it would have, if acting long enough, to produce an arbitrarily great motion. But this does not happen. The velocity which a weight falling to the earth can attain has a maximum value. It amounts to 11,200 meters per second. For this is the value of the velocity which would be acquired by a weight of mass m falling to the earth of mass T from an infinite distance. The total "fall-force" *(vis viva)* acquired in gaining this maximum velocity G is mG^2 [It should be the kinetic energy $\frac{1}{2}mG^2$, but Mayer always uses *vis viva*—Ed. note.] The "fall-force" associated with a smaller separation distance can be readily calculated as a fraction of this maximum. For heights in the neighborhood of the earth* the numerator of this fraction is the distance of fall, while the denominator is the radius of the earth. In a fall from a height of 15 feet the *vis viva* gained is therefore mG^2 (15/19,600,050) or the velocity attained on reaching the ground is $G\sqrt{15/19\,609\,050}$. If the weight falls from infinite distance to a height of 15 feet above the earth's surface then 1,299,999/1,300,000 of the total *vis viva* has been gained, 1/1,300,000 of this still remains left and it is with the expenditure of this comparatively small amount of *vis viva* that the mass m gains its velocity of 30 feet per second in falling. It is clear that the motion of a falling body provides no exception to the axiomatic rule of the proportionality of motion and energy expenditure. The *vis viva* expenditure is zero only when the weight

---

* In general the numerator is the height from which fall takes place. The denominator is, however, the product of the original distance of the center of mass of the two bodies (earth and falling body) with the distance left over, treating the earth's radius as unity. A weight which begins to fall from height h has at height h' the velocity $G\sqrt{(h-h')/h \cdot h'}$.

merely presses down but does not move. A constant energy which brings about effects without changing (decreasing) does not exist in physics.

Experience shows on all sides the transformation of mechanical effects into heat. The decisive facts here, the development of heat by collision and friction, are old and have been known for a long time. Are they, however, for this reason less compelling? We observe the heating of the great mill stones and of the flour in the grist mill, the heating of the great driver and the linseed oil in the oil mill, of the wood in the dye mills, the never-ending heating of the axles of all wheels in motion. We remember the famous experiments of Rumford! Everywhere we note the same phenomenon: endless heat production with the expenditure of mechanical activity. [As is well known, Joule and Colding actually used the heat developed by friction to measure the mechanical equivalent of heat—Ed. note.]

The author made some observations on four pulp cylinders in a paper factory. In each cylinder there were about 80 pounds of paper pulp and 1200 pounds of water. The temperature of the pulp went up steadily from the beginning of the motion. The surroundings were at temperature 15 °C: in 32 to 40 minutes the temperature of the pulp went up from 14 °C to 16 °C. The highest temperature observed after several hours of processing was 30 °C. If we calculate that by the exertion of a horsepower in 1 minute 2700 pounds are raised 1 foot, the heating of 1280 pounds of water (not counting that of the apparatus) by 1 °C in 16 minutes is the equivalent of 3.16 horsepower. This agrees sufficiently well with the approximate estimate of the engineers that in the running of a pulp vat about 5 horsepower is needed. Does the mechanical effect of the 5 horsepower in the machinery go to zero? The actual fact is that it is transformed into heat.

The most important physical laws which relate to the transformation of motion into heat can be briefly summarized as follows:

1. Negative motion like negative matter is an imaginary quantity. The destruction of positive motion by negative is a paradox.

2. Just as the quantity of matter is measured by absolute weight [He really means mass—Ed. note.] so the measure of motion is the product

of the mass by the square of the velocity [he really means $\frac{1}{2}mv^2$ or the kinetic energy]. The Cartesian law: force equals the product of mass by velocity is false and was shown to be so by Leibniz.

3. Just as portions of matter of opposite qualities, such as an electropositive base and an electronegative acid, can neutralize each other, so motions in opposite directions can neutralize each other. The continuing entity changed in quality but unchanged in quantity is the neutral salt in the first illustration and heat in the second.

4. The relation in which the quantities of neutralizing matter or motion stand with respect to each other is as a rule not one of equality. This depends rather on the nature of these objects. Acids and bases neutralize each other when the quantities are proportional to their combining weights; motions in opposite directions neutralize each other when the quantities are proportional to their velocities. In this neutralization and in the production of motions the velocity plays the role of combining weight. In mechanics this law is introduced under the name of "principle of virtual velocities" [or virtual work].

4

A fourth way in which physical energy can appear is electricity. Frictional electricity is produced by the application of mechanical action.

We have before us an electrophorus of ideal perfection. The cover has the weight P. The cover is at height h above the region of influence of the under-disk. By the use of an appropriate balancing weight the cover can move up and down freely above the under-disk. Then whether the disk is electrified or not the top cover can move up and down without loss of mechanical energy as long as no electric charge is withdrawn from the under-disk (or base). The situation is otherwise when the electrophorus *works*. If the cover is lifted up from the non-electrified base, the work done against the balancing weight P is Ph. If the base is electrified, the cover is attracted and the corresponding work is greater than Ph, say $Ph+p$. The cover is able when lying on the underdisk to exercise an electrical effect. Let us suppose this has happened, the energy corresponding to it is definitely determined. Let us call it z. Now the attraction is increased even more and to raise the cover requires even greater weight than before. The work of the resultant weight will be greater than $Ph+p$. Let us call it $Ph+p+x$. If the cover is raised to h again, we get a second electrical energy which we may call z', etc. In every descent the work that is won is $Ph+p$, while in every rise to h, the work lost is $Ph+p+x$. Thus while on each trial we apply or expend a mechanical energy x, we win the electrical energy $z+z'$. Hence we must have

$$x = z+z'.$$

The conclusion is simple. Out of nothing we get nothing. The resinous electricity cannot by itself have produced the continual production of electrical energy, since it remains undiminished in amount. The mechanical energy which disappears in each repetition of the charging process cannot have vanished to zero. What then remains to say, if one does not wish to get involved in a double paradox, except that the mechanical energy has been transformed into electricity?* The base of the electrophorus, like the lever or the retort, is nothing more than an

---

* From the closer inspection of the quantity x in the equation $x = z+z'$, it develops that the quantity of electrical energy is proportional to the square of the electrical potential (Spannung). *Proof:* Let the given negative electrical potential of the hard rubber disc of the electrophorus be denoted by S, the potential of the positive electricity of the cover plate $= S/q$, where q is a constant, which approaches unity. The magnitude of the attraction or repulsion of two electrically charged bodies is, according to the direct measurements of Coulomb, equal to the product of their potentials. The attraction between the positively charged cover plate and the negatively charged hard rubber base is accordingly S^2/q, or proportional to the square of the potential of the base. Since now the attraction between cover and base is at every distance of separation inversely proportional to the square of the distance the mechanical energy $p+x$ which must be expended to separate cover and base to a distance h must be proportional to S^2. We now see that the ratio p/x as well as the ratio z/z' is independent of S and accordingly $p+x$ as well as z and $z+z'$ as well as z' are proportional to the square of S or the square of S/q. Since, however, $(S/q)^2$ is equal to the square of the positive potential of the cover when raised to height h, while z' is the electrical energy obtained by the cover when it is raised to height h, the electrical energy varies as the square of the potential and the magnitude of the total electrical energy is equal to the product of the surface by the square of the potential.

instrument which the experimenter uses to bring about a meta-morphosis.

A pendulum set in vibration will continue to move back and forth without loss of amplitude if friction and air resistance can be neglected. However, if a metal pendulum bob (insulated electrically from its surroundings) is permitted to swing near an electrified non-conductor and if periodically sparks are drawn from it while it is in the region of influence of the charged body, the amplitude will be observed to grow smaller: the mechanical energy of the pendulum motion will be successively transformed to electrical energy.

The production of frictional electricity also takes place with the expenditure of mechanical energy. The materials rubbed together are held fast to each other by the attraction of opposite charges. But the necessary separation to produce free electric charges cannot take place without the expenditure of mechanical energy. It is well known that in the production of frictional electricity there is no frictional heat developed. [A doubtful statement—Ed. note.] In the transmission of electricity the attraction relations just discussed are reversed and by the expenditure of electrical energy mechanical energy is produced. In every contact a part of the electricity is neutralized, more or less as motion is in inelastic collisions. The most important laws associated herewith are the same as those mentioned above in connection with the neutralization of motion. Mass and velocity in motion become replaced by surface area and potential respectively in the case of electricity. The dynamics of motion can be reduced to the consideration of two forms of energy, namely motion and heat, and is therefore simpler in its representation than electricity, which must consider three energy forms, motion, heat and specific electrical energy.

In analogy with the production of electricity, magnetism can also be produced by the expenditure of mechanical energy. A given magnet here plays the role of the electrophorus. Through the magnetization of a previously unmagnetized steel bar the same attraction relations ensue as those considered above in the case of the electrophorus. The result is similar: expenditure of mechanical energy leads to the pro-duction of electric and/or magnetic potential.

5

The spatial separation of a mass from the earth we have learned above to consider as a form of energy [potential energy]. A gram of mass at infinite* distance from the earth or, as we shall choose to say, at infinite mechanical separation from the earth, represents a form of energy. By the expenditure of this energy, that is through the mechanical joining of the two masses, another form of energy is produced: the motion of 1 gram of mass with the velocity of 34,450 feet per second. By the expenditure of this energy of motion 1 gram of water could be raised 14,987 °C. [This is unrealistic. What Mayer means is that by the expenditure of the above amount of mechanical energy 14,987 calories of heat can be produced—Ed. note.]

Experience now teaches us that the same energy effect can be gained from a chemical combination of certain materials as from a mechanical joining, that is to say, the development of heat. The presence of chemically different substances or rather the chemical differences of various portions of matter constitute a source of energy.

The chemical combination of 1 gram of carbon and 2.6 grams of oxygen is approximately equivalent in order of magnitude to the mechanical joining of a particle of mass 0.5 gram and the earth. In the former case 8500 calories of heat are produced and in the latter case

* The concept of infinite separation is to be taken here in its physical and not in its mathematical sense. It is to be understood in terms of the physical limit of the earth's gravitational field. Such a limit is not mathematically realizable (save at infinity). But physically we may introduce it with the same right with which we introduced a limit to the electrical atmosphere surrounding a charged conductor. For example, if we call a distance of 10,000 earth diameters an effectively infinite distance, this is sufficiently accurate for practical purposes. The mathematical representation of gravitational phenomena must begin with the consideration of either a very large or very small space and must go from these to concrete measurable spaces by slight increases or slight decreases. Neither of these methods can completely replace the other. From the physical standpoint, however, the method which begins with the infinite magnitude has the decided advantage that the true nature of the attraction, that is its decreasing intensity with distance, has already been taken into consideration. It is only in this way that the connection, the inner unity of mechanical, electrical and chemical processes can be completely clarified. The other method begins with the destruction of the physical concept of attraction, since it considers the attraction at infinitely small distances as effectively constant.

7400 calories. The chemical combination of 1 gram of hydrogen with 8 grams of oxygen (it being assumed with Dulong that the heat of combustion of hydrogen is 34,743 calories per gram) is in order of magnitude equivalent to the mechanical combination of a mass of 2 grams with the earth. In the former case the heat developed is about 34,700 calories. In the latter case it is about 30,000 calories.

For relatively small separations and low velocities the energy associated with mechanical effects falls far below that connected with the better known chemical combinations. The situation is otherwise, however, if we look beyond our immediate surroundings into space.

Of all terrestrial substances the detonating mixture of oxygen and hydrogen provides the greatest amount of heat energy when the combination takes place. When 1 gram of the mixture explodes to water, 3850 calories of heat are produced. The combustion of 1 gram of a carbon and oxygen mixture yields 2370 calories. Since, however, 15,000 calories of heat must be expended to separate a mass of 1 gram completely from the earth, it follows that on the earth no chemical difference exists through whose expenditure as much heat can be obtained as by the joining of a mass particle with the earth from a great distance. On the other hand, on the moon only 777 calories of heat correspond to the separation of 1 gram of mass from the moon.

The earth moves in its orbit about the sun with an average velocity of 93,700 feet per second [The German foot used by Mayer is somewhat larger than the English foot—Ed. note.]. In order to produce this motion by the combustion of carbon, an amount of carbon 13 times the mass of the earth would have to be burned. The quantity of heat connected with this would be in calories equal to 110,000 times the mass of the earth in grams. A small fraction of the kinetic energy of the earth's motion in its orbit would be sufficient to disintegrate the earth into the particles composing it. If we assume, however, that a particle equal in mass to the earth were resting on the surface of the sun, in order to remove this load and put it into motion in the present orbit of the earth with the earth's orbital velocity (the average distance of the earth from the sun = 215 times the radius of the sun) it would be necessary to supply 429 times greater energy expenditure or to burn a mass of carbon equal to 5557 times the mass of the earth.

Since the energy of chemical reactions seems to be insufficient to bring about the above-mentioned effects, it may well be asked how we can conceive of an energy expenditure which was sufficient to bring about the planetary motions in the first place? Let us assume that in "the beginning" the earth was at rest at distance from the center of the sun equal to 430 times the radius of the sun and that from here it fell the equivalent of 215 radii of the sun into its present orbit. It would then have attained its present motion. We can make similar statements about all the other planets. The major axes of their orbits provide a measure for the initial distances of the planets at rest from the sun. The major axes are the expression for the magnitude of the mechanical energy of each planet given to it by the creator. They stand as firm in this respect as all past time.

If we ask why the planets which we have assumed to be originally at rest did not fall directly onto the sun's surface and why the planets with almost invariably small eccentricity move about the sun in the same plane and in the same direction, it is clear that one hypothesis after another must be the answer, for:

"That is the curse of a wicked deed,

That it must ever more bring forth more evil."

It is worthy of note that there are compounds whose decomposition takes place with the development of heat and mechanical energy. Such compounds do not originate by themselves alone, but come about only in connection with chemical processes which are accompanied by a release of heat. We must assume that the heat which arises in the one compound, in chemical phraseology, in the nascent state, partially goes into the detonating compound. If an equal mass of chlorine gas combines on the one hand with a solution of ammonium chloride and on the other hand with a solution of ammonia itself, the heat developed in the second case, as the author found, is much greater than in the first. The reason for this must be sought in part in the fact that in the formation of nitrogen chloride heat becomes "latent" and this latent heat is later liberated as free heat and mechanical energy in the ultimate decomposition [by explosion].

The decomposition into chlorine and hydrogen as well as the combination of chlorine and nitrogen to form a compound both correspond to liberation of *energy*. Let us compare with these certain mechanical relations. A raised weight represents an expenditure of energy. A dropped weight which by the expenditure of a further mechanical effect compresses a stiff spring on which it falls and is then propelled upwards again by the expansion of the spring, represents in its deepest significance the expenditure of energy. [It is assumed that external resistance or damping is absent—Ed. note.] However, we find nothing analogous to the action of the spring and the damping in chemical combinations, for the elasticity of chlorine and nitrogen after they have become freed of combination cannot be compared with the compression of the spring, in so far as this elasticity is a consequence and not a cause of the liberated energy in the decomposition.

If one attaches plates of zinc and copper to insulating handles and then brings them into contact and immediately thereafter separates them, the zinc plate will be found to be at a + potential and the copper plate at a — potential. Before contact the metals were neutral (non-electrified), after contact they are charged oppositely. In order to bring about their separation, the expenditure of mechanical energy is necessary, just as in the somewhat analogous case of the electrophorus, previously discussed. Other circumstances prevail if the plates remain in contact. In place of mechanical energy, chemical energy enters. With the expenditure of the chemical separation of metal and oxygen there arises a whole summation of effects, as we have already considered in detail. By means of the lever we can transform a given fall-force [*Fall kraft*] into another. We sacrifice a given spatial displacement in order to bring about another spatial displacement. The wonderful lever of the chemists is the voltaic pile. Reduction phenomena and the development of heat and mechanical energy, which we see arising as effects of the pile, owe their origin to their expenditure of a form of energy, to the given displacement of metal and oxygen, of salt and acid. The equivalence of cause and effect is brought out most effectively by the gas apparatus of Grove.

If we now combine the results of all these investigations into a single general law, we once more obtain the axiom originally set up. This is:

In all physical and chemical processes the energy involved remains constant.

The following scheme provides a summary of the principal forms of energy already considered.

I. Potential energy (due to gravity) (fall-force)
II. Energy of motion
   A. Simple
   B. Vibrational
III. Heat
IV. Magnetism
   Electricity (galvanic current)
V. Chemical separation of certain materials   ⎱ Chemical
   Chemical combination of certain other materials ⎰ energy

On this formulation of the five principal forms of physical energy there follows the task to demonstrate the metamorphoses (changes) in these forms by means of 25 experimental examples. From the most important and simplest facts we assemble here the following:

1. The transformation of one fall-force into another by means of the lever.

2. The transformation of fall-force (potential energy) into motional energy, either by free fall or by falling along a prescribed path.

3. The transformation of one motion into a second motion. This can take place completely through the central collision of elastic particles of the same mass or incompletely through collision and friction.

4. The transformation of energy of motion into fall-force (potential energy) through the motion of a particle upwards from the earth's

97

surface. Such a transformation of both forms of energy can take place periodically as in the vibration of a pendulum and the central motions of the planets.

5 and 6. Transformation of mechanical energy into heat in the compression of elastic fluids, and by collision and friction. The absorption of light consists in a transformation of vibrational motion into heat.

7 and 8. The transformation of heat into mechanical energy follows from the expansion of gases under pressure, in steam engines, and in the vibrating energy in the radiation from heated bodies.

9. The transformation of one kind of heat into another by means of conduction.

10. The transformation of heat in chemical reactions. If compounds are decomposed by heat they are formed with the development of heat. Examples are the combination of sulphuric acid with water and the combination of lime with water.

11. The transformation of chemical energy into heat as in combustion.

12, 13, 14. The transformation of chemical energy into the galvania current and the further transformation from the current into chemical energy as well as the transformation of the current into chemical energy in the voltaic pile.

15, 16, 17. The transformation of electricity into heat and mechanical energy: in the glowing of a wire conducting current, in the electric spark, the motions of electric and electromagnetic attractions, by electric discharges, especially in the lightning flash.

18. A partial transformation of one electric current into another giving rise to an induced current.

19. The direct transformation of heat into electricity in the phenomenon of thermoelectricity and in the production of cold through the Peltier effect.

20, 21. The transformation of mechanical energy into electricity by friction and induction.

22–25: The transformation of mechanical energy into chemical energy, indirectly through the transformation of the given energy into electricity and heat.

It is prejudices, sanctioned by age and widespread dissemination, as well as primary sense impressions with their ambiguous yet so persuasive evidence, which seem to contradict the principles set forth here, and not the natural phenomena themselves. Against such prejudices we call to witness the history of all sciences.

While we vindicate the right of motion to exist as an entity and to represent substantiality, we must unconditionally deny the material nature of heat and electricity. For would it not be too absurd to look to a fluid for the nature of motion and the displacement of mass or to wish to assign in alternation now a material and now an immaterial nature to the same object?

Let us speak out the great truth: there are no immaterial materials! We realize that we are fighting a struggle with a deep-rooted hypothesis, canonized by high authority; with the imponderables we intend to abolish the last remnants of the gods of Greece from the study of nature. But we also know that nature in its simple truth is greater and more majestic than any structure built with the hand of man and all illusions created by the mind.

In terms of human conceptions the sun is an inexhaustible source of physical energy. The stream of this energy which also pours over our earth is the continually expanding spring that provides the motive power for terrestrial activities. In view of the large amount of energy which our earth is continuously emitting into space in the form of wave motion, its surface without continuous replenishment would soon revert to the cold of death. It is the light of the sun which when transformed into heat brings about the motions in our atmosphere and raises the waters of the earth to the clouds on high and brings about the flow of rivers. The heat which is produced through friction by the wheels of wind and water mills is sent to the earth by the sun in the form of radiation.

Nature has set itself the task of catching this light streaming to the earth in its flight and to store it up when transformed to another form. For the attainment of this end Nature has covered the earth's crust with organisms which while living absorb the sunlight and by expenditure of this energy can produce a host of chemical reactions.

These organisms are the plants. The world of plant life forms a reservoir in which the fleeting sunbeams are trapped and are, so to speak, laid down in ingenious fashion for usufruct. This is an economic solicitude with which the physical existence of the human race is inseparably connected and which through the appearance of a rich vegetation arouses in every eye a feeling of well being.

The reducing reactions which sunlight produces in both inorganic and organic substances are everywhere known. Reduction reactions occur most strongly in bright sunlight, more weakly in the shade and fail altogether in darkness and candle light. According to what has been said above they rest on the transformation of one form of energy into another, on the transformation of mechanical energy into chemical energy.

It was not very long ago that the controversy raged whether plants during their lifetime are able to transform chemical elements into other elements or even to create them. Some facts and experiments seemed to affirm this result, but more precise tests have taught us the contrary, and science has now pronounced with assurance a unanimous "No" to the question. We know that the materials by which a plant grows and those which are eliminated by the plant are in sum equal to the materials absorbed. The tree which now weighs several thousand pounds has absorbed every grain of matter from its environment. There takes place in plants only a transformation of matter and not its creation.

This principle forms the bridge connecting chemistry and plant physiology. Its truth is more obvious *a priori* than through actual experimental investigations, which at any rate do not allow objections to be raised to it in individual cases. The same grounds force us to assume that plants are able merely to transform energy and not to create it.

Plants absorb energy in the form of light and produce from this chemical energy. The principle of sufficient reason makes it necessary for the scientist to bring the output into causal connection with the input. This input, or the light absorption as we have known since the time of Nicolas Theodore Saussure (1767–1845), is a necessary requisite for the output, the chemical reduction process.

In the first place it must now be asked whether the light which falls on living plants really finds another application than light which falls on dead bodies. That is, whether the plants, other things being equal, are heated less strongly by light than other dark surfaces. The results which observations on a limited scale in this field have provided appear to fall within the limits of error of such investigations. On the other hand the commonplace experience that the heating effect of solar radiation on broad expanses of countryside is checked by nothing so effectively as by rich vegetation, even though the plants on account of the dark color of their leaves must absorb a much larger part of the sunlight falling on them than the bare ground. If, therefore, the evaporation from the plants is not sufficient to explain this fact, the above question must be answered without contradiction in the affirmative.

The second question concerns the cause of the chemical reactions brought about through the plants. These reactions, i.e., the transformation of certain chemical compounds into others, constitute, as above set forth, a form of physical energy. This is equal to the heat won through the combustion of the plant. Now does this energy arise from a vital or life process without the intervention of some definite form of energy? The creation of physical energy for itself alone is hardly thinkable. It appears all the more paradoxical if we consider the experiential fact that it is only with the help of sunlight that the plants are in a position to make their contribution. All further investigation would be cut off by the assumption of such hypothetical action of "vital energy", and it would render impossible the application of the laws of the exact sciences to the study of life phenomena. Acting against the spirit of progress which manifests itself in the science of the present time, its proponents will be led into the chaos of the unrestrained play of fantasy. The author therefore believes that he can reckon on the intelligent understanding of his readers if in the following investigation he lays down this principle as having axiomatic truth: *that during life processes only transformations of matter and energy take place and never the creation of either.*

Admitted then that the production of chemical activity (in plants) cannot take place without the corresponding expenditure of another form of energy, the further question arises whether this energy supply comes only from the consumption of sunlight or whether it does not flow from another source? The conjecture that plants absorb free heat from their surroundings and with its help could bring about chemical changes would, to be sure, be an obvious one. However, experience contradicts this conjecture. It teaches that heat by itself alone is not in a position to maintain the required chemical processes. The absorption of light accordingly remains the *sine qua non* of these processes. The ability of plants to bring about a transformation of physical energy appears to be limited to the metamorphosis of light (and of electricity).

At the time of germination, in the dark and in part during fertilization, vegetables absorb oxygen and emit in turn an almost equal volume of carbon dioxide. The chemical energy expended here must bring about the production of another form of energy. What is this form of energy?

Two cases may be thought of as possible here. Either the chemical activity is transformed into free heat, as is detected during fertilization, or the plants expend, somewhat in the fashion of a voltaic pile, a certain amount of chemical energy to bring about other chemical processes which cause a consumption of energy, processes that may consist in the decomposition or combination of substances. In the latter case no heat will be eliminated in the plants, at any rate not the heat corresponding to the oxidation of carbon.

If one keeps in mind the nightly recurring formation of carbon dioxide by the plant, one finds it improbable that these organisms in the achievement of their important task to accumulate energy should not only not be assisted but should even be interrupted by the mathematical–geographical relations of the aspect they present to their surroundings. Plants, by expending in the dark for the emission of heat a part of the carbon won during the light, would by day take two steps forward and by night one step backwards. If we take into consideration that thanks to the small inclination of the earth's axis to the ecliptic and thanks to the rotation of the earth the most regular apportionment of day and night falls in the zones of most luxuriant vegetation, and that the absorption of oxygen in the dark is necessary for the life of the plant, it appears to be more probable that the energy won during the nocturnal oxidation of carbon finds its more important application in the plant than that this energy should be exuded in the form of free heat. Continued investigations in the field of physiological chemistry on the night life of the plant and exact experimental determinations of the heat of combustion of vegetable substances will alone be in a position to cast the necessary light on this rather obscure subject.

The physical energy assembled through the activity of plants devolves upon another class of creatures who take to themselves this supply of energy by robbery and expend it for their own purposes. These are the animals. The living animal absorbs continuously combustible material coming from the plant kingdom in order to combine it again with the oxygen of the atmosphere. Parallel to this expenditure runs the output characterizing animal life, the production of mechanical effects, such as motion and the lifting of weights. This output is both means and end in the animal organism; it is the fundamental condition for the animal life process. Plants indeed also produce mechanical effects; they move and they lift. However, it is clear that for the same time and the same mass the sum of the effects produced by an individual plant is vanishingly small compared with the animal output. Whereas in plants the production of mechanical effects plays qualitatively and quantitatively a very subordinate role, the transformation of chemical energy into individually useful mechanical energy is the inseparable accompaniment and the characteristic feature of animal life.

The magnitude of the mechanical output of an animal is conveniently expressed by a weight which can be raised to a certain height by this output. We calculate that a horse, by the voluntary exercise of its muscles for 8 hours during the day, is in a position to raise 27,000

103

pounds (each of 500 grams) 1 Paris foot or 4400 kilograms 1 meter in each minute. Per hour the output will be 1,620,000 pounds raised 1 foot, in 1 day 12,960,000 pounds raised 1 foot. In metric units these figures become 260,000 kilogram meters and 21,100,000 kilogram meters respectively. We can express every other transient or continuous energy output of an animal as an appropriate fraction or multiple of the output of our normal horse. What holds for the one must of course find its application to the other.

In the animal organism a sum of various forms of chemical energy is continuously expended. During life ternary and quaternary compounds suffer the most important changes in their composition and are for the most part again eliminated after a short time in the form of binary compounds as materials of combustion. The magnitude of this energy, or respectively the quantity of heat which can be released by these processes, has been in no way satisfactorily evaluated by experiment. However, it is satisfactory enough here, where it is mainly a question of establishing a principle, to carry out the calculations using the heat of combustion of pure carbon. The numerical values obtained in this way can be corrected by very simple reduction when in the future experimental physics yields more exact data on the energy-supplying activity of the chemical reaction in question.

We take as the heat of combustion of carbon the figure (after Dulong, see above) 8558 calories per gram. This means that the combustion of 1 part by weight of carbon corresponds to the raising of 3,600,000 parts by weight to a height of 1 meter. If we now express in terms of mass of carbon the expenditure of chemical energy which a horse must make to achieve the above figure we find that the animal will need for mechanical purposes 580 grams of carbon in 1 day, or 72 grams in every working hour of an 8 hour day, or finally 1.2 grams per minute of the working day.

According to current estimates the power production of a strong working man is one-seventh that of a horse. A man who in a working day does work equivalent to the raising of 300,000 kilograms 1 meter must expend for this purpose 83 grams of carbon. Per working hour this amounts to about 10 grams or for 1 minute about 170 milligrams of carbon. A bowler who throws a 4 kilogram ball with a velocity of 10 meters per second expends energy to the amount $\frac{1}{2}mv^2 = 200$ kg m²/sec². This corresponds to 20 meter kilograms weight. Since the heat of combustion of 1 milligram of carbon = 3.6 meter kilograms weight, this corresponds to the combustion of about 6 milligrams of carbon. A man who lifts his weight of 72 kilograms 5 meters up in the air needs for this purpose the burning of 0.1 gram of carbon. In climbing a mountain 3000 meters high the energy expenditure of such a man is about 60 grams of carbon, neglecting the dissipative loss associated with every step.

If the animal organism were able to expend the combustible material at its disposal for mechanical purposes alone, the calculated quantities of carbon for the times mentioned above should suffice. However, in reality associated with the production of mechanical effects in animal bodies there is a steady production of heat. The chemical energy which is contained in the food introduced into the body and the oxygen which is breathed is accordingly the source of two energy manifestations—motion and heat. The sum of the physical energies produced by an animal is equal to the magnitude of the energies associated with the chemical processes taking place simultaneously.

If one sums up the mechanical energy manifestations produced in a given time by an animal this is ultimately changed by friction or other dissipative processes into heat. If we add this heat to that produced directly by the body in the same time, we shall obtain precisely the quantity of heat which in and for itself corresponds to the chemical processes that have taken place. To assume on either side a plus or minus is forbidden by the law of sufficient reason. From nothing, nothing comes; nothing leads to nothing *(Ex nihilo nil fit; nil fit ad nihilum)*.

The only cause of animal heat is a chemical process, in essence an oxidation process.

It is the great and well-recognized merit of Liebig to have defended the truth of this principle, resulting from the discoveries of Lavoisier, against the doubts and criticisms that were raised. Where it is a question of the confirmation of a miracle, that is the *creation* of physical energy, the famous experiments of Dulong and Despretz cannot lay claim to the least demonstrative power. And indeed, aside from the limits of error of such investigations, the reasons for this are as follows.

1. Since breathing runs in parallel with the chemical activity in animals, it must then be assumed that a warm-blooded animal at rest and breathing in unhindered fashion must produce as much heat as is necessary to maintain its bodily temperature constant. If now an animal goes from a state of free respiration to one in which respiration is stopped, or cut down, the production of heat is lessened, and the animal during a given period of time will lose more heat than it produces. In the investigations of Dulong and Despretz the animals during a 1–2 hour experiment were in a state of reduced respiration produced by fright. As a consequence they had, during this time, to lose more heat than was produced in them and hence they had to lose some of their natural internal heat (Liebig).

No justified doubt can be raised about the correctness of this argument. Everyone knows the objective temperature variations of the body surface in different states of feeling. Effects having a depressing influence on the feelings lower chemical activity in the body: the skin tends to cool, for more heat is lost than is produced. The highly interesting investigations of Scharling (*Annalen der Chemie von Wöhler und Liebig*, vol. XLV) demonstrate directly the dependence of chemical processes in the animal body on transient inner states. A 10-year-old girl in a state of light nausea breathed out much less carbon dioxide than before and after this occurrence and indeed in the ratio of about 5 to 8.

Now to presuppose that the animals in the investigation of Dulong and Despretz did not have their respiration rates altered continuously by fright, and on a small deficiency to found the great conclusion of the miracle effect of "vital" energy—this procedure does not really deserve the name scientific. When further Kohlrausch (*Physiologie und Chemie in ihrer gegenwärtigen Stellung*, Göttingen, 1844) expresses the opinion that the quantity of water presupposed to be in the apparatus could introduce a corrective influence due to a disproportion between production and dissipation of animal heat, he only shows thereby that in his polemic against Liebig's argument he has fallen into error.

2. Dulong and Despretz in their investigation determined the amount of atmospheric oxygen consumed as well as the quantity of carbon dioxide formed. They then proceeded to calculate the quantity of oxygen used up in water formation. They accordingly proceeded on the assumption that all the oxygen available for combustion originated entirely in the atmosphere. But since metabolism in animals does not consist merely in the exchange of carbon and oxygen in inorganic form but more particularly in the decomposition of ternary and quaternary oxygen compounds, herein lies a possible source of error. Organic materials can liberate heat through chemical changes without taking up oxygen. This is proved by the process of spirituous fermentation. If one had added to the animal under the apparatus a flask of fermenting grape juice and had then, following Dulong and Despretz, compared the heat developed with the loss in atmospheric oxygen, the discrepancy between the calculated and the observed heat would have come out even larger.

3. In their research Dulong and Despretz assumed values for the heats of combustion of carbon and hydrogen that were too small. Later direct experimental determinations of heats of combustion by Dulong and others show this. Liebig (*Annalen der Chemie von Wöhler und Liebig*, vol. LIII) has called attention to this decisive circumstance and at the same time has shown that after taking into account the necessary corrections the difference between observation and calculated results disappears!

From what has been cited we can satisfy ourselves that the valuable investigations of the above-named scientists, far from containing any contradiction of the fundamental principle *ex nihilo nil fit*, actually have confirmed experimentally the truth these scientists attacked. These investigations teach us that a chemical process, namely one of combustion, runs parallel to the production of animal heat and that the heat developed corresponds precisely enough to the oxidation of hydrogen and carbon. On the other hand, they do *not* teach us that the liberated heat is in reality greater than the chemical process is able to produce. And least of all do they teach us to recognize the share of the heat created by the "vital" process. If this share were actually once established and if indeed a qualitative difference were shown to exist between the heat produced by chemical processes and that "created" by the so-called "vital" process, then and only then would the time come to return to mysticism and to doubt the possibility of a purely scientific treatment of the phenomena of life.*

In the actively exercising animal, metabolism is greater than in the resting animal. Let the magnitude of the chemical processes taking place in a given time interval in a resting individual be x, whereas it is $x+y$ in the active individual. If now during the work the same quantity of free heat were liberated as in the case of rest, the contribution y of chemical energy would have to correspond precisely to the production of mechanical effects. On the average, however, the actively working organism will produce more free heat than one at rest, since the increased respiration rate itself brings about an increased heat loss which must be compensated by an increased production. During the exercising period, therefore, x plus a part of y will be expended as heat, whereas the rest will appear as mechanical energy.

It becomes clear from this that the production of mechanical energy must stand, in a certain degree, in antagonism with the production of heat. Thus the greater the fraction of y expended for the production of heat, the less will be available for transformation into mechanical energy, and conversely.

Common experience teaches us this. It is a well-known rule that to go far one must begin with slow steps. The proverb says: "make haste slowly" *(Eile mit Weile)*. The worker seeks to avoid transpiration in order to conserve his energy, and the driver does not like it when his horse becomes "warm". In everyday life we say that sweat wastes energy. In scientific language this means the increased production of

* To see what strange ideas the so-called vitalists are reduced to today, one may cite among others Reich's *Lehrbuch der praktischen Heilkunde nach chemisch-rationellen Grundsätzen* (Berlin, 1842). Reich considers animal heat to be an inheritance given to the newborn at birth. For this bright thought we wish the gentleman in question a parlor stove which expends for ever and ever the heat passed on from Father Blastfurnace!

heat takes place at the expense of mechanical energy. Under the same circumstances of consumption the phlegmatic temperament, both in man and animals, is in a position to yield the greatest efficiency.

We shall return later to this competition existing between the production of heat and mechanical energy. It must now be demonstrated that according to experience the increased expenditure of combustibles by the working individual really contains the necessary energy to bring about motion.

A strong horse that day in and day out is allowed to rest will be richly nourished with 7.5 kilograms of hay and 2.5 kilograms of oats per day. If, however, this animal has to lift 2,100,000 kilograms up 1 meter every day it can obviously not exist on this nourishment.

In order to keep this horse in good conditions we provide him with $5\frac{1}{2}$ kilograms of oats per day extra. Now the above 10 kilograms of food (proportional to the previously mentioned quantity x) contains 4.037 kilograms of carbon according to Boussingault (*Annales de Chemie et de Physique*, vol. LXX) and Liebig *(Die organische Chemie in ihre Anwendung auf Physiologie und Pathologie)*. The 5.5 kilograms of oats which corresponds to the quantity y according to the same reckoning contain 2.367 kilograms of carbon. According to Boussingault, the ratio of the introduced carbon to that in the combustible form is about 3938 : 1364.4. Computed in this way x, that is the amount of carbon burned by the resting animal, $= 2.6383$ kilograms while $y = 1.547$ kilograms. The carbon used for mechanical energy, according to the above, amounts to 0.58 kilogram, which we set equal to z.

Now the following ratios emerge: (1) the mechanical output to the total energy production $= z/(x+y) = 0.14$; (2) the mechanical output to the extra production of the working animal $= z/y = 0.37$; (3) the heat production in the resting animal to that in the working animal $= x/(x+y-z) = 0.73$.

According to Liebig *(Die organische Chemie in ihrer Anwendung auf Physiologie und Pathologie)* the prisoners in the jail in Giessen, who indulge in no activity, receive the equivalent of 26 grams of carbon daily. The ratio of the total carbon introduced to the unburned amount, according to Liebig, can be assumed to be approximately

290/12. According to this, the amount of carbon oxidized daily by a prisoner = 255 grams. A soldier in a garrison enjoys daily a ration of 453 grams of carbon (see Liebig also). If we spare to our worker for the completion of his task another 110 grams, he will then absorb 563 grams of carbon or will burn up according to the above ratios 540 grams of carbon.* We get accordingly the following ratios: (1) mechanical energy to total energy = 82/540 = 0.15; (2) mechanical output to the extra production = 82/285 = 0.3; (3) heat production at rest to heat production while working = 255/(540−82) = 0.56.

In these calculations only the transformed carbon is taken into consideration. If we set the heat of combustion of the food taken into the body equal to that of the carbon and hydrogen contained in it, we can take the heat of combustion of the hydrogen to be added in to be about a quarter that of the carbon. It is to be understood, however, that the magnitude estimates given here can lay no claim to general validity. The output and consumption must show great fluctuations associated with the individual constitution and conditions of life. Nevertheless, these results can serve to confirm the following conclusions as established by experience.

1. The increased consumption which the working organism makes of combustible material, even when one keeps the plus of the heat produced in mind, is sufficient to account for the production of mechanical energy in a natural way.

2. The carbon used up by the vigorously active mammal for mechanical purposes will hardly amount to one-fifth of the total consumption. The remaining four-fifth will be consumed in the production of heat.

In order to be able to accomplish the transformation of chemical energy into mechanical energy, animals are equipped with specific organs which are entirely lacking in plants. These are the muscles.

* The numbers found by Lavosier, Andral and others are significantly smaller. Respiration experiments must obviously give minimal values since they can only be carried out with resting individuals.

For the manifestation of activity in a muscle two things are in question: (1) the influence of a motor nerve as a condition of the activity, and (2) metabolism as the cause.

As in the case of the whole organism, the muscle as an organ has its psychical as well as its physical side. We count the nerve influence as representing the former and the chemical process as representing the latter. The motion of a steamship obeys the will of the helmsman and the engineer. The mental influence without which the ship would never get into motion or would indeed go to pieces on the next reef, certainly guides but does not of itself move the ship. For the continuous motion, physical energy is needed, provided by the coal. Without this the ship stays dead despite the strongest will of its pilot.

In the first part of this essay the role played by the combustion process in inorganic equipment to produce motion, namely the steam engine, was developed in its principal points. It is our present task to consider the various life phenomena in connection with their physical causes and to apply these considerations, gained from exact science, to the formulation of physiological principles.

Muscle is only the tool by means of which the transformation of energy is brought about; it is not the actual material which has to be transformed in order to bring about the performance of work. From what has been said above a vigorously active man transforms in one day 82 grams of carbon into mechanical energy. If we set the mass of the muscle structure of a man weighing 75 kilograms equal to 30 kilograms, after deducting the 77 per cent water content there remain about 7.5 kilograms dry combustible muscle substance. If it is assumed (even if not wholly admitted) that the heat-producing energy of this material (with 40 per cent oxygen and nitrogen) is equivalent to that of pure carbon, the whole muscle structure of the man would have to be oxidized in at most 13 weeks if it as to provide the *material* for energy production.

The above arithmetical deduction gains greater significance if we consider the performance of a single muscle, namely that of the heart. In accordance with the information provided by Valentin (*Lehrbuch der Physiologie des Menschen*, Vol. 1, p. 488), we take the quantity of blood supplied by the left ventricle in every systole as having the average value 150 cubic centimeters. We also take the hydrostatic pressure of the blood in the arteries (according to Poiseuille) as equivalent to 15 centimeters of mercury. The mechanical energy provided by the left ventricle in one systole can be computed from this. It is equal to that involved in the raising of a mercury column 1 square centimeter in area of cross-section and 16 centimeters high to a height of 150 centimeters. The weight of the mercury is 216 grams. The energy associated with one systole is therefore equivalent to the work of raising 325.6 grams to a height of 1 meter; which is further equivalent to 0.766 calorie of heat or equivalent to the combustion of 0.09 milligram of carbon. If we reckon that there are 70 heart beats per minute or about 100,800 beats per day, the mechanical energy provided by the left ventricle in 1 day is equal to 32,810 kilogram meters or 77,200 calories of heat, corresponding to the combustion of 9.02 grams of carbon. According to Valentin, the performance of the right ventricle is half as great as that of the left. The mechanical energy provided by both chambers in one day is therefore 49,200 kilogram meters, corresponding to 115,800 calories of heat or the combustion of 13.5 grams of carbon.

If we take the weight of the whole heart as 500 grams of which 77 per cent is water, there remains 115 grams of dry, combustible material. If as above we set this matter as equivalent to pure carbon, it follows that if the organ had to sacrifice its material content to its energy performance it would have to be oxidized in at most 9 days. If indeed we take the two ventricles alone, weighing 202 grams, according to Valentin's measurements, on the above reasoning the total consumption of these chambers would be completed in 4 days!

The assumption of a quick transformation (combustion and renewal) of the active muscle fibers stands in apparent contradiction to the physiological facts and microscopic observations. The above numerical values (4 days to 13 weeks) are evidence that no substantial part of the combustible material used up for the energy performance can originate in the muscle fibers themselves.

Animal tissues like their constituent parts (carbon, hydrogen and nitrogen) show at ordinary temperature only a very slight tendency to combine directly with oxygen. Dried membranes if exposed to atmospheric air or an atmosphere of oxygen remain unchanged for years on end. Even if such a tendency is assumed, the entrance of oxygen into the tissues, in particular the muscle fibers, which are chiefly in question here, is hardly permitted. The oxygen gains access to the arterial blood in the depths of the organism in bound or combined form. If it had any tendency to form binary compounds with organic material it would without doubt choose the parts lying most closely to it as it finds them present in full measure and in dissolved form in the blood itself. There is no understandable reason why the combined oxygen should free itself from the arterial blood and should penetrate by osmosis the blood vessel walls in order to seek out the muscle fibers.

One can turn to a specific "vital energy" with apparently greater plausibility as a protection against another form of chemical action, namely the decomposition which the organic parts suffer after death. The decomposition of organic compounds by fermentation and putrefraction, as they take place in certain temperature ranges in the presence of water and partly with and partly without the absorption of atmospheric oxygen, is a process which up to a certain point takes place with increasing acceleration. In this respect the decomposition can be appropriately compared with the fall toward the earth of a body from outer space. Such a body approaches the earth with increasing acceleration. At a certain sufficiently great height the smallest thread would have been able to check the fall of a heavy mass, whereas in the later course of the motion toward the earth the greatest obstacle is unable to check the plunging weight.

If we kill a perfectly healthy animal and a few days after death find the corpse in a state of rapid decomposition, it is true that we can feel motivated to introduce philosophic reflections on "vital" energy, which was able to check the mighty process of decomposition. In truth,

113

however, in such meditations we run the risk of taking a spider web for cable rope. It is one thing to prevent by anticipation the starting of a conflagration, it is another to put a stop to raging elements. In the first minutes or hours after death the tendency toward decomposition is very slight (and the initial attraction in the mechanical process of fall corresponds to this tendency). It grows through its own action, through the presence of putrified material. In the living organism mathematical laws guarantee that this tendency is still smaller than in the minute after death. In life the tendency toward decomposition is vanishingly small. The force with which we have to oppose this tendency is proportional to the tendency and hence is also vanishingly small: it is in effect zero.

A vessel full of freshly pressed-out grape juice will in a short time be in full fermentation if exposed to heat in the presence of oxygen. Let us suppose, however, that by a suitable arrangement the products of fermentation are continually removed at the moment of their formation. (This can be done in part at any rate by the continuous filtration of the whole mass.) In this way, by the small daily addition of fresh grape juice it would be possible to keep the vessel full of sweet fermentable mass. As long as the flow out and in continues to be balanced in regular fashion, general net fermentation can never take place.

The eminent engineer, Mr. E. Schaufellen of Heilbronn, has fitted up an aspirator in the stack of a steamship, a wheel which, driven by the machine itself, draws a strong stream of air through the burning coal in the boiler and thus facilitates the emergence of the combustible material in the form of binary oxygen compounds without the appearance of soot or black smoke. This apparatus rests on a happy imitation of the life process: a small part of the mechanical energy produced at the expense of the heat of combustion is applied to facilitate mechanically the entrance of oxygen and thereby to prevent the formation of inappropriate products.

Countless devices are constantly busy in the living animal in filtering and aspirating the bodily chemical processes, in part through the expenditure of mechanical energy, so as to increase the intensity of these processes, to decrease their magnitude, to deposit the waste products in separate specific volumes and to remove these at once, and above all to discourage the formation and accumulation of putrid ferments. If, however, one brings into the lymph system of the strongest man a grain of rotting liquid manure, neither nature nor art can set any bounds to the quickly following disintegration, to the deadly fever. Where is here the "vital" force or energy? Where the ability to develop resistance against external causes of disturbance? *Hic Rhodus, hic salta!*

It is a fact known for a long time that liquids which in and for themselves have a tendency toward spontaneous dissociation can remain for a long time undecomposed in the inside of a living body. We accordingly ask: is the resistance of liquid organic materials against disintegration considered from the chemical standpoint much greater in general than that of solid parts?

If we bypass the "vital" force idea, we can easily and simply explain the relations in question.

If stagnating liquids* in contact with living forms remain unchanged for a long time, whereas without such contact but under otherwise similar circumstances they decompose, we must conclude from this that the solid parts through secretion and reabsorption exercise an influence through which these liquids maintain their composition purely by chemical laws. We recall here what was said previously, as an example, about the fermentable grape juice remaining sweet. This necessary assumption of reabsorbing and secreting activity of the surfaces surrounding such a liquid is in agreement with well-known anatomical, physiological and pathological relations.

In accordance with their different chemical condition, liquid materials possess a very different tendency toward spontaneous decomposition. Thus milk, wine, fatty oil and absolute alcohol behave very differently in this respect. The richer in organic constituents the material included in the body is, the greater will be its tendency to decompose. The interaction between the surrounding solid parts and the enclosed liquids or the absorbing and secreting activity of the cavity

* We shall discuss later on the case of circulating body juices like the blood and the lymph.

walls must now be the greater, the greater the decomposability of the included matter. Since this activity in turn is proportional to the relative amounts of the parts in question, it therefore follows that the decomposability of the exudates is proportional to the vascularity of the surrounding membrane.

The decomposability and vascularity are present in minimal degree in the normal liquids of the eye, the so-called aqueous and vitreous humors and the corresponding surroundings. Both decomposability and vascularity are also rather small effects in certain dropsical complaints. Then after repeated tappings of the abdominal and chest cavities the exudate becomes richer in organic matter, the serous skin at the same time becomes thicker and richer in blood. The bile and the easily decomposable milk are surrounded by a mucuous membrane full of vesicles. In the absence of excretion they can remain undecomposed for long intervals. In their anatomical and physiological behavior the mucous membranes are like abscess walls. After opening of an abscess, atmospheric oxygen gains entrance to the suppurated liquid inside and thereby the tendency to decomposition is without doubt increased. For the prevention of the decomposition the blood content of the abscess walls and the interaction of solid and liquid parts must be increased. One recalls here the operation to relieve emphysema.

If the pathological process at a particular place has lasted a certain length of time, if it has reached a certain extent, it communicates, as experience teaches, a tendency toward decomposition to the whole lymph mass. The abnormal alteration which one part of the blood has continually to undergo in the abscess walls in order to try to prevent the decomposition of the pus will, after a long continued spreading, lead to a consumptive fever.

If the pus in its wandering and spreading comes in contact with a bone surface, at this place it will be deprived of its protective envelope (similar to the mucous membrane) and so it will get the opportunity to putrify. The bone will then either be drawn into the decomposition process or in more favorable cases it covers itself with skin having many blood vessels, it becomes granulated and the pus gains a better condition.

The extravasation of blood from the blood vessels, if not reabsorbed in a short time, can only avoid bad decomposition through the agency of walls full of vessels and by an increased secreting and absorbing activity. This decomposition, however, results without fail in the cotton plugs to check hemorrhaging in the nasal and genital cavities.

The law of the numerical relationship existing between the tendency toward decomposition on the one hand and a necessary chemical process on the other hand must hold not only for stagnating patholo-gical collected exudates, it must also find application to liquids* in general, to their transformation and to the whole organism and basal metabolism as a whole. The formation of carbon dioxide in the living organism, as an expression of metabolism, cannot decrease beyond a certain point without putting the animal body in danger of disintegra-tion. This physiological minimum of the chemical process must have different values for different temperatures. The tendency for animal matter to decompose, as is the case with fermentation, is greater in warmth than in cold. Animals which at rest form only as much carbon dioxide as is essential to maintain their lymph in equilibrium, that is animals which satisfy themselves with the minimum of the chemical process, must form more carbon dioxide in a warm environment than in a cold one. This is the reason for the observations of Treviranus and others that in cold-blooded animals and those mammals which hiber-nate, the carbon dioxide production increases at once with temperature increase, whereas this goes the other way round with animals having constant body heat.

Since we see in a chemical process, namely the basal metabolism, a complete ground for the continued existence of living organisms, we must raise a protest against the introduction of a special "vital" force or energy in order to explain the phenomena of life.

For a long time there has been no prospect that we should succeed in achieving the correct explanation of states of sickness. Liebig's theory of disease, although it aroused sanguine hopes in many physici-ans, has not brought us a single step nearer the goal. In this branch of

---

* The solid parts of matter under normal circumstances and with exclusion of free oxygen have without doubt a very small tendency toward decomposition.

science the investigations of a Lotze or a Wunderlich have been able to achieve only negative results. We may more easily find the *quintessence* than solve the problem of a series of natural processes by mere suppositions.

With the absorption of atmospheric oxygen and the formation and secretion of binary compounds there takes place continuously in the animal organism a chemical process whose effect we have learned to recognize as the production of heat and mechanical energy.

In order in the first place to assure ourselves of the place where combustion occurs, a thermometric measurement of the various organs and the different forms of the blood would appear to provide the simplest means. Heat is continuously drawn out of the lungs by the introduction of cold air and by the evaporation of water. Since, however, the lungs show no lower temperature than the other central organs, and at the same time the aerated blood is no colder than the venous blood, we must conclude that there is development of heat in the lungs. According to Holtzmann it takes 564 calories of heat to vaporize 1 gram of water at 37.5 °C. The vaporization of water in the lungs, taken to be about 500 grams in 24 hours, produces cooling to the extent of 282,000 calories. If we further assume that in the lungs 12,000 cubic centimeters of air are heated through 20 °C, and if we take the heat capacity of air as 0.267 calories per gram °C and its specific gravity or density as 1.3×10^{-3} grams per cubic centimeter the amount of heat per day involved in this is 120,000 calories. If we add to this the 282,000 calories above, the total is 402,000 calories of heat extracted for this business. Assuming that for each systole 100 cubic centimeters of blood is accommodated by the heart, if we take a heart beat rate of 70 per minute, it follows that in one day 10,080,000 cubic centimeters of blood pass through the lungs. If we take the heat capacity and density of blood equal to that of water we find that the blood of the pulmonary artery for an external temperature of 17.5 °C must be on the average 0.04 °C warmer than that of the veins in the lungs *if no heat were to be developed in the lungs*. If we now calculate that the mechanical energy produced by the right ventricle is transformed into heat in the lungs, we then find this frictional heat of the lungs (consider again the discussion above) equal to 38,000 calories. If we subtract this from the above-mentioned 402,000 calories, the temperature difference in question cannot be more than about 0.025 °C.

If, on the other hand, we agree to place the heat production exclusively in the lungs and take the heat-producing chemical process as large as possible, that is equal to the combustion daily of 500 grams of carbon, namely 4,279,000 calories, it would follow that after the subtraction of the 402,000 calories mentioned above, 3,877,000 calories of thermometrically perceptible heat would be produced daily. If the heart capacity is again taken on the small side as 100 cubic centimeters per beat, it follows that the venous blood in the lungs must be about 0.04 °C warmer than the blood in the pulmonary artery. If the heart capacity is taken as 150 cubic centimeters per beat the corresponding temperature difference becomes 0.25 °C and the temperature of the lungs must exceed that of the other internal organs of the body by the same amount.

The above investigations on the temperature difference of the two kinds of blood have, as is well known, not led to results on which there is general agreement. If we take into consideration the fact that the circulation and oxidation relations in an animal subject to vivisection will doubtless deviate from the norm, and that the blood-rich principal cavities of the body protected against loss of heat (and also of course the blood streaming out of them) must constantly manifest a higher temperature than the outer parts of the organism and the blood returning from these, we shall readily understand the observed temperature differences between arterial and venous blood; these in many actual cases significantly exceed the maximum values of 0.25 °C to 0.4 °C above calculated, and in no way justify definite conclusions as to the place where heat is developed.*

Chemical activity and the development of energy take place in the lungs as well as in the other parts of the body, as we shall see. The blood

---

* Mayer (*Meckels Arkiv*, Vol. 3, p. 337) found that the blood of the carotid artery is 1–2 °R warmer than the blood of the jugular vein. On the other hand, he could find no temperature difference between the blood in the two halves of the heart.

takes up oxygen in the lungs and carries it to all parts of the body. The chemical activity follows on the consumption of this oxygen. With the stopping of respiration the change in the color of the blood ceases, as well as heat production and muscular motion. With what physical components of the arterial blood does the oxygen combine? What matter serves the organism as fuel? Does the chemical activity in question take place *inside* the blood vessels or does it extend over the cavity walls to the surrounding solid tissue?

Of the blood that the left ventricle of the heart sends out, the greater part returns to the right auricle without having left the blood vessels in its wandering through the body. Because of the action of the heart, however, the blood exerts a continual pressure against the vessel walls, and thereby a part of the blood, and indeed the watery part, is driven out through the walls. In the reticular capillary vessels the hydrostatic pressure of the blood against the blood vessel walls must be nearly uniform and this pressure must tend to hinder the part of the blood pressed out from re-entrance into the blood vessels, while the end-osmotic and exosmotic tendencies hold each other in equilibrium, so far as external effects do not intervene. But now there are other tubes present in which the pressure produced by the heart ventricle is absent and these are prepared to absorb the extravasated liquid, namely the lymph.* This tube system is called the lymphatic system.

There can be no doubt that the growth and regeneration of living tissue can be brought about only through the protein- and salt-carrying liquid exuded through the walls of the blood vessels. The question here, however, is the following: does this fluid play an important role in the oxidation processes in question or not? In order to decide this point we must fix our attention on the quantity of the lymph exuded

---

* The demonstration of the connection between the blood fluid and the lymph is due to Müller (*Handbuch der Physiologie* Vol. 1, 1st ed., p. 245). The lymph exuded from the blood vessel system is introduced into the comparatively wide openings of the lymphatic vessels by the pressure coming from the heart, and is further carried through these vessels. Attenuating pressure through muscular contractions accelerates the streaming of the lymph as in the case of venous blood. [A rather lengthy medical and physiological discussion on this footnote follows, which is here omitted—Ed. note.]

from the blood. Magendie pierced the *ductus thoracicus* of a dog which had just been fed and obtained on the average in 5 minutes 15 cubic centimeter of lymph from which for the purpose in question the chyle was removed. If we apply this quantitative measure to the living conditions of a healthy man, we are justified in assuming that for such an individual the *ductus thoracicus* would not provide more than 100 centimeters of pure lymph in a time interval of 5 minutes. In the same time interval, however, the left ventricle, whose capacity is assumed to be 100 cubic centimeters per beat, will transport a quantity of fluid 350 times greater. From these incidental estimations, in which the action of the secretion-producing organs may conveniently be left out of account, we can conclude with assurance that of the fluid exuded by the left ventricle not even 1 per cent (perhaps not 0.1 per cent) leaves the blood vessels; this means that of 100 parts of circulating fluid 99 and a fraction parts complete the circuit from left to right ventricle without leaving the blood vessel system. The physiological facts teach us then that the blood of a warm-blooded animal returning from the various parts of the body without renewed take-up of oxygen is not in a position to carry out the chemical process in the body. This means that the oxygen taken up in the lungs in every circuit is completely or almost completely applied to the maintenance of the chemical process. If we are now willing to assume that the atmospheric oxygen transported from the lungs to all parts of the body is distributed uniformly over the blood fluid, or put in another way, if in spite of all chemical and physiological facts we were inclined to neglect or negate the important role which the blood corpuscles play in chemical processes in favor of the lymph, it would still have to be maintained that not even 1 per cent of the atmospheric oxygen taken up gets out of the blood vessels. This means that *not the 100th part of the oxidation process takes place outside the blood vessel walls*.

This principle has been directly confirmed by physiological observations. The necessary and immediate consequence of any stopping of the oxidation process is the cessation of the production of heat and mechanical energy and in due course the initiation of decomposition. In general, this happens, for example, with the closing off the trachea and locally as well through the ligature of individual arteries and veins. The blocking of the thoracic duct (lymph vessel system), on the other hand, produces quite a different effect from the closing of the trachea. It immediately causes lymphatic exudation and destruction of the "chilopoese". Since now the motion of the plasma existing outside the blood vessels after blocking of the thoracic duct immediately must find a goal, with the oxidation process nevertheless still continuing, we may draw from this the conclusion that this *liquor extra muros* (fluid outside the walls) must in any case have a very subordinate role to play in the oxidation process. The center of this process is the center of the blood vessel system. The blood, a slowly burning fluid, is the "oil in the flame of life".

Unmistakably the solid parts of the organism, the blood vessel walls and other tissue parts, in particular the nerve fibers, exercise a great influence on the chemical changes of the blood. Through this influence in general the intensity of the oxidation process is increased and the affinity is raised. Everyone knows that in countless cases chemical reactions are conditioned by the mere presence of certain materials which themselves have no part in the reactions taking place (catalysts). If without making any assumptions we want to assign a name to a well-established fact we can designate the role which the unchanging material plays in such phenomena with the expression "contact influence". As is well known, it has also become customary to speak of "catalytic force" and "catalytic effect". With the word "force" here one is to understand only the "measurable cause proportional to a measurable effect" and hence on logical grounds one is not to insinuate a specific "force" for this phenomenon.*

Blood reddened by oxygen and left to itself retains its bright color unchanged for a long time. However, it loses it immediately during its

---

* A force is called catalytic in so far as it stands in no numerical relation to the effect in question. An avalanche starts in the valley: a gust of wind or even the shrill note of a bird may be the "catalytic force" which gives the signal for the fall and the propagated destruction. The catalytic nature of this "force" rests entirely in logic and the causal law.

progress through the capillary vessels of the body. Apparently the blood also suffers a chemical change under the contact influence of the blood vessel walls. This influence makes itself noticeable only in the finer vessels in which the area of the surfaces in contact in comparison with the size of the tubes themselves is increased almost to infinity. This capillary diffusion of the blood takes place in the lungs as well as in the rest of the body and it becomes clear from this that the conditions for chemical activity are present in the lungs as well as elsewhere in the body.

The living blood consists of two mechanically, chemically and physiologically distinguishable components, namely on the one hand the fluid plasma, liquor sanguinis, and on the other hand the powdery blood corpuscles. The blood plasma has only a very slight tendency if any to absorb oxygen gas, while the blood corpuscles on the contrary have a great tendency to do this. This well-known situation leads to the conclusion that it is the blood corpuscles which absorb atmospheric oxygen in the lungs. It follows from this that the vital chemical process rests essentially on the fact that the oxygen absorbed by the blood corpuscles combines with the combustible blood components to form carbon dioxide and water. The blood corpuscles play in this connection a role like that of oxide of nitrogen in the preparation of sulfuric acid, namely an oxygen carrier.

That the organic matter in the blood corpuscles takes part in the combustion process, that they little by little break down into binary compounds, cannot be doubted. Certainly, however, the greater part of the combustible material originates in the fluid part of the blood. If we estimate the quantity of blood in an average man as 10 kilograms and the normal amount of blood corpuscles at 127 parts per 1000 (after Andral) this provides 1270 grams of blood corpuscles whose carbon content (at roughly 50 per cent) can be taken then as 635 grams. If now the production of carbon dioxide were to take place at the expense of the blood corpuscles alone then the whole mass of these would be burned up and have to be renewed in approximately 2 days. In anemia the number of blood corpuscles frequently drops to half the normal value, at times even to merely a sixth part. The total conversion must in this case be brought about in much shorter time.* The difficulty with which the blood corpuscles reproduce themselves stands in irreconcilable contradiction with the assumption of such a rapid physiological change.

The blood corpuscles, analogous to carbon and other porous materials, possess the capacity to absorb gases. Oxygen is indeed much more strongly absorbed by them than carbon dioxide. On this behavior rests the physiological action of these organic components. Liebig (in his famous work *Die organische Chemie in ihrer Anwendung auf Physiologie und Pathologie*, Braunschweig, 1842) derived this property from the iron content of the corpuscles and assumed that in the black blood the metal is present in the form of suboxide, whereas in the red blood it is present as the red oxide of iron. This is an ingenious and precise theory which allows all chemical and physiological facts to be brought into agreement.

If black blood is brought in contact with oxygen the blood corpuscles absorb the oxygen and thereby become red. The iron-free blood fluid, on the contrary, holds itself at first indifferent to the presence of oxygen. The absorbed arterial oxygen can be made to combine with organic matter to form carbon dioxide and water through circumstances of two kinds. In the first place this can happen in the presence of surplus or excess oxygen, and in the second place it can happen through the mere contact influence of the blood vessel walls and the organs of the body.† In the first case, if for example blood containing much atmospheric air is shaken vigorously and is therefore brought into repeated contact, the blood remains bright red and the carbon dioxide

---

* Under otherwise equivalent circumstances with the decrease in the number of blood corpuscles there must go a decrease in the take up of oxygen as well as of the process of combustion and the production of heat. Nature, however, has a means of counteracting this injurious decrease in chemical activity: the pulse beat becomes faster and turbulent, the circulation is accompanied by special murmurs, respiration is strenuous, the individual blood corpuscles take up oxygen with increased vigor and hence it is not seldom that people afflicted with this desease show a florid appearance. This explains also the plethoric state of the chlorotic invalid—a symptomatic complex which not unreasonably has been designated *febris alba* (white fever).

† Gradually this process also takes place by itself in the blood released from the arteries.

formed is released in the form of gas. In the second case the blood becomes black and the carbon dioxide formed is absorbed by the blood corpuscles. Both causes conditioning the transition of the oxygen to the bodily organic substance, that is to say, the presence of excess oxygen and the contact influence, take place in the lung simultaneously. Under these circumstances a part of the absorbed oxygen must wander along with the arterial blood as through a conductor, while the rest remains in the blood corpuscles and produces their red color. The former part forms carbon dioxide and water from the organic material of the blood, while the latter part takes the place of the venous carbon dioxide of the blood corpuscles and all the carbon dioxide is ultimately expelled through the excess oxygen, perhaps by the agency of the law of diffusion.

Since under the contact influence of the lung capillaries the carbon and oxygen content of the flowing blood exerts an influence tending to withdraw oxygen from the blood corpusles, it could be foreseen that the latter are not able to saturate themselves completely in the lungs. We find, for example, that the lungs of a stillborn child are reddened to a greater degree when air is blown into them than healthy lungs are through ordinary respiration.

Every individual in the course of his life is often exposed to external changes, and if life and health are to be preserved the chemical process in the body must simultaneously now increase and now decrease. The oxygenation of the blood corpuscles in the lungs and the reduction process in the rest of the body must be able to take place at differing rates under different circumstances. The whole process must be able to move within not too narrow limits. On this rests the tolerable range of health.

Observations which I made in the Tropics taught me to recognize the role which the blood corpuscles play in the combustion process in the body. In a sea voyage of 100 days, out of a passenger list of 28 there occurred no serious incidence of sickness. However, a few days after the arrival in Batavia (Dutch East Indies) there broke out an epidemic of an acute catarrhal inflammatory affection of the lungs. In the ample blood-letting which I carried out, the blood from the veins

125

in the arm had an unusually red color, so that if I had judged by color alone I might have thought I had struck an artery. At the same time the blood was very rich in fibrin*, the cake sticking fast to the walls of the dish (in which the blood was placed). After 12–16 hours usually only a few spoonfuls of serum had separated out. Never, however, did any crusta phlogistica show itself. After 3 weeks, during which we had sailed to Surabaya, the chest illness disappeared, but then dysentery appeared along with acute hepatitis which along with the contagion attacking from the black *schönen* accompanied our ship all the way back to the Cape of Good Hope. Since the military physicians at the Simpang hospital on Surabaya had indicated to me that the section of the veins in acclimatized Europeans was hazardous, I limited myself almost entirely to local blood-letting. In a copious venesection which I performed 2 months after our arrival in Java on a heavy seaman who had been attacked by hepatitis I found a normal black color of the blood.

From the laws set forth earlier it follows of necessity that the temperature difference between the internal heat of the organism and the heat of the surrounding medium must stand in a definite numerical relation with the difference in color of the two kinds of blood, that of the arteries and that of the veins. The greater this temperature difference, the greater must be the color difference. This color difference is an expression of the magnitude of the oxygen consumption or for the intensity of the combustion process in the organism.

We recall here the temperature and color relations of cold-blooded animals, of the hibernator, as well as the animal fetus, and those afflicted with cyanosis. We recall also the bright red color of the blood which Thaekrah observed when he bled a patient in a warm bath. Finally we recall the difference in color of the venous blood in the different seasons of the year, well known since the work of Autenrieth. The observations mentioned above belong indeed in this category. In

---

* An exception was provided by a marine, Bornet. Spared from the chest affliction, he had however fallen a victim to an attack of syphilis, against which among other things two venesections had been brought into application. The blood was dark black but poor in fibrin.

the open sea the temperature difference (between body heat and environment) amounted to about 15 °C, the air was in motion and hence cooling in its action. On the Java coast, however, the difference on the average was scarcely 5 °C, the air was seldom in motion and usually quite stagnant. Nature therefore had the task of decreasing the chemical process to a corresponding degree, and this took place immediately: the arterial blood corpuscles in the capillaries of the body were only incompletely reduced, whence the arterial color of the venous blood. After longer residence in the tropic zone, however, other conditions appear. Following an altered influence of the lung tissue on the blood contained in their capillaries and in consequence of a change in the lungs which we are not in a position to describe in detail and probably also in consequence of a chemical change in the blood corpuscles, in the acclimatized individual these become the carriers of a smaller quantity of oxygen, and while earlier the venous blood approached the arterial blood in redness, now the arterial blood through its blackness becomes similar to the venous blood in the colder regions, the redness in the cheeks is lost and the acclimatized European finally takes on the well-known atrabilious facial color.

Just as the leaf of a plant changes a given form of energy, namely radiant energy in the form of light, into another form of energy, namely chemical, so the muscle in the animal organism produces mechanical energy at the expense of the chemical activity in its capillary vessels. In the case of plants free heat is not able to provide a substitute for the solar radiation nor in the case of animals does it provide a substitute for the chemical process. Every animal motion goes on with the consumption of oxygen with the concomitant formation of carbon dioxide and water. Every muscle, to which access of atmospheric oxygen is cut off, suspends its functioning.

While the fibers flex themselves and the muscle shortens without changing its volume, work is done, occasionally very significant and then again to a smaller degree. At the same time there takes place in the muscle capillaries an oxidation process corresponding to heat

127

production. By the action of the muscle a part of this heat is made "latent" or spent, and this expenditure is proportional to the work done, that is, either the product of a weight raised by the height to which it is raised or the product of the moved mass by one-half the square of the velocity attained (the kinetic energy). In general, then, this expenditure is proportional to the mechanical energy produced. To use a well-known terminology, the muscle uses heat in *status nascens* to do work.

We are unable to state further in any precise fashion the method by which the muscle as an organ carries out the transformation of chemical activity into mechanical energy. In countless cases these transformations of matter and energy via inorganic and organic routes are going on before our eyes and yet each of these processes provides an impenetrable mystery to human cognition. It is a task of practical value for science to establish a rigorous indication of the natural limits of human inquiry. The attempts to penetrate into the depths of the world order by the use of hypothesis form a sidepiece in the strivings of the learned.

If we know the amount of work a muscle does, we also know *ipso facto* the amount of the applied chemical energy. However, the actions of a rather large number of muscles are combined in most voluntary motions. The amounts of work which a single muscle can do in different contractions are of such different magnitudes that it is difficult to abstract general quantitative determinations from special cases.

Of the work done by the heart and the consumption of energy by this organ some approximate calculations were given earlier. We shall compare an arbitrary muscle action, namely that of the gastrocnemius muscle (the large muscle in the calf of the leg) in which we shall use as a basis the figures given by Valentin in his *Lehrbuch der Physiologie des Menschen* (1844). We assume that a strong man standing on one foot can by a sufficiently strong contraction of this muscle raise his bodily weight 13 centimeters off the floor. In this case the point of the sole of the foot corresponding to the lengthening of the middle attachment of the Achilles tendon becomes separated from the floor by about 4.5 centimeters. If we assume that the weight of the man is

75 kilograms, the work done by the contraction of the three muscles, gastrocnemius, soleus and plantaris, is the equivalent of that needed to raise 2030 grams 1 meter. This is equivalent to the burning of 0.538 milligram of carbon or 4.77 calories of heat. Now Valentin estimates the mass of the three muscles in question as 896.9 grams. From this we estimate the mass of the red blood contained in the capillaries of these muscles as about one-fifteenth of the mass of the flesh itself, say 60 grams. The carbon content of fibrin and albumin amounts to 2.7 grams. It follows, therefore, that in a single strong contraction the carbon used up is about 1/15000th of that in the capillary plasma of the active muscle.

The amount of oxygen necessary for the combustion of the above 0.558 milligram of carbon comes to 1.47 milligrams. We now assume with Liebig that the iron in the red blood occurs more or less as ferric oxide while that in the black blood occurs as ferrous oxide. We then find that the 45 milligrams of iron oxide in 60 grams of blood give up 4.8 milligrams of oxygen in their transfer through the capillaries of the muscles in question. This amounts to more than three times the amount needed, as shown above.

We must consider in this calculation that a part of the oxygen supplied combines with hydrogen to form water and that this part gives somewhat more heat than that produced in the formation of carbon dioxide (about in the ratio 4/3), and further through the reduction of the ferric oxide to ferrous oxide and through the combination of the carbon dioxide with the ferrous oxide some heat on the one hand becomes latent and some on the other hand becomes free. Finally there is the additional point that we do not know the heat-producing ability of organic materials, but can only estimate it from their carbon and oxygen content and therefore must remain uncertain as to the role which the integrating oxygen plays in the production of heat. From all this it develops that in this business only approximate results can be obtained. In any case the muscle work production could be taken large enough and the quantity of blood small enough with respect to the chemical process to be able to draw from reasonable figures the certain conclusion that the chemical process is in reality more than sufficient to take care of the necessary performance of work. Yes, we must indeed state with the highest probability the law that the muscle even when contracted to the utmost is not in a position to transform into mechanical work all the energy resulting from the chemical process without at the same time developing free heat. In other words, the chemical process is always greater than the useful effect. The same situation is found to exist in inorganic devices for changing heat into mechanical energy, namely steam engines and cannons.

The energy production of the left ventricle of the heart was shown above to be equivalent to the work done in raising 325.6 grams 1 meter or put in another way equivalent to 0.3256 meter kilograms. Reduced to the same mass the ratio of the energy produced by a single contraction of the leg muscle to that of a single heart beat is

$$(2030)(136) : (325.6)(896.9) = 20 : 21.$$

In combination with the muscular contraction dynamics of Schwann and others, this result leads to the principle that the work done by a single contraction of a muscle is proportional to the mass of the muscle, and therefore to the number of primitive fibers in its length. This thesis, which recommends itself through its simplicity and internal likelihood, can however find no application in the case which involves continuous production of work by different muscle parts. Let us take again the mass of the left ventricle (according to Valentin) as 136 grams and the mass of the whole voluntary muscle system of the body as 32 kilograms. We set (as above discussed) the daily work performed by the left ventricle at 32,810 meter kilograms and the daily mechanical energy output of the muscle system at 300,000 meter kilograms. Then the ratio of the output of the heart to that of the rest of the muscle system, mass for mass is

$$(32,810)(32,000) : (300,000)(136) = 25 : 1.$$

Hence mass for mass, the daily output of the heart is 25 times as much as the rest of the voluntary muscle system. This means that even

130

during the working day of 8 hours the heart is three times more active as the rest of the muscle system.

The predominance of the heart when compared with the energy output of a single group of muscles can be shown most emphatically as follows. If standing on one foot one raises his heel 4 centimeters off the ground (with the use of the *musculus gastrocnemius, soleus and plantaris*, with the exclusion of the use of the *musculus tibialis, posticus*, and *peronaeus longus et brevis*) the energy expenditure (easily afforded by anyone) corresponds approximately to one heart beat. However, if one wishes to continue to perform this work isochronously with the heart beats, one will soon be forced to refrain from this concurrence with the heart, since the muscle gets so lame that it will refuse to serve even the strongest will. After a short rest, however, the work can begin again. The fact here is known to everybody; its correct explanation is a physiological problem of importance, and follows at once from our previous considerations. It presupposes for the muscular activity a corresponding supply of atmospheric oxygen and arterial blood. Since now the reappearance of the consumed material is tied to a certain time interval, the sum of the energy expenditures finds a limit which must not be exceeded in a given period. If the supply of arterial blood corpuscles in the muscle capillaries is used up, the corresponding activity is at an end. In a single contraction the expenditure capability will be more or less proportional to the quantity of blood which is usually present in the capillaries of the resting muscle—the blood supply which in turn stands in a definite relation to the mass of the muscle. When, however, it comes to the sum of the energy expenditures which the muscle can produce in longer intervals, the original quantity of blood loses its significance and in its place comes into question the greater or less ease of its continual replacement. In other words, the productivity of the muscle depends only on the quantity of *circulating* blood. *Hence the capacity for energy expenditure is proportional not to the mass of the muscle but to the mass of the circulating blood.* The momentary expenditure depends on the myological (muscular) condition of the motion-producing apparatus whereas the long-term expenditure depends on the angiological (vascular) conditions.

131

The heart, which sends blood to all other organs of the body, has initially thought of itself as cheap in this distribution. Two arteries of comparatively considerable size supply the arterial blood of its substance, and the circulation velocity of this blood is greater than in all the other organs of the body. This follows from the place of origin of the coronary artery at the beginning of the aorta, from the shortness of the path which the blood has to travel and from the arrangement of the nerves of the heart. The latter discharge themselves into a common cap-like orifice *(ostium venae magnae)* directly into the right ventricle and so offer a significant surface for breathing. For this reason, while the venous blood of the other organs has to contend with a centrifugal pressure, the blood of the heart is pushed out in a centripetal direction.

If the heart is stimulated to increased action by the regulators of its action, namely the nerves which emanate from the spinal cord, it is provided immediately, through the increased energy expenditure, with the larger amounts of necessary material. On the other hand, when activity is much diminished the circulation in the heart itself takes place more slowly and this organ can still continue to supply chemical energy and to work even if the pulse beat at the wrist has long since ceased to be perceptible.

In contrast to the heart, called upon for such great activity, the pad of flesh with which Nature has covered our backs is marked by its lazy behavior, its small daily energy expenditure as well as by its relative paucity of blood vessels. The muscles at the extremities of the body, however, lie somewhere in the middle with respect to their capacity for energy expenditure and their richness in blood vessels. Between these and the heart lie the indefatigable intercostal (rib) muscles and the diaphragm. Through exercise the muscles become full of blood; in the resting state, however, they become pallid. Muscles which through whatever circumstances remain for some long period incapable of service degenerate into a bloodless mass. With wise economy Nature follows the fundamental principle: whoever does not work shall not eat. The womb when denuded of blood is incompetent to expend energy. When rich with blood it can carry out strong contractions. The walls of the blood vessels themselves actively need an arterial blood supply. Through mere elasticity no mechanical energy can be produced. Therefore the yellow elastic fibers are able to fulfill their purpose without receiving functional blood.

The oxidation taking place everywhere in the capillaries of the body produces a corresponding quantity of heat. The muscle at rest behaves here like any other motionless component. The active muscle, on the other hand, expends combustible material for the production of mechanical energy. In every muscular action heat becomes "latent" (in *status nascens*). If now the passage of blood and the chemical activity are not strengthened simultaneously with and in proportion to the expenditure of energy, the production of heat in the muscle must be smaller when work is done then in a muscle at rest.

If the energy expenditure is equivalent to raising 75 kilograms through 2.7 centimeters, the latent heat amounts to 5 calories. If now this energy expenditure as has been assumed above follows as the result of the contraction of 896.9 grams of muscle substance the heat lost by this mass of muscle or a single contraction is $5/896.9 = 1/180$ calories. (It is here assumed that the heat capacity of flesh is equal to that of water.)

In work that continues for time this heat defect accumulates and can be detected observationally. What was said above about the antagonism of the production of heat and work in general applies here. Douville (*Journal de Chimie médicale*, Vol. viii, February) found the following temperature values in a Negro:

1. Lazy and inactive in his cabin: 37 °C.
2. Lazy and inactive in the sun: 40.2 °C.
3. Active in the sun: 39.75 °C.

If one begins to work very hard physically in very cold weather, one notices a feeling of cold in the active parts of the body. A man sawing wood in winter frequently alternates his hand (for even through his gloves his hands get cold), until he has sufficiently warmed up his working arm. The saw blade gets hot. We know precisely the origin of this heat: it is ultimately due to the oxidation in the capillaries of the muscle. An active smith can by his hammer bring a cold piece of iron to a glowing state. This heat, however, appears at the expense of the temperature of his arm. *Ex nihilo nil fit.*

The heat deficit during work would be even more noticeable and the ability to produce energy of the voluntary muscles would be restricted to narrow limits were it not for the fact that chemical activity is increased both in general as well as locally. If one opens a vein in a part of the body when the local activity is strenuous, the blood rushes out in correspondingly increased quantity. Activity of respiration and blood circulation are correspondingly enhanced if the organism produces mechanical energy. In every strenuous work effort breathing and pulse rate accelerate, and indeed the more strongly the weaker chemical activity takes place in the resting individual. This follows on readily comprehended grounds. An energy expenditure that costs a strong, healthy person only a few breaths can demand turbulent increase in respiration and circulation, suffocation sensations and heart palpitations in a person with low blood count and of chlorotic, scorbutic nature.

But even the strongest human beings and animals in the strenuous production of mechanical energy, for example in the very fast climb of a height, get into the situation where breathing is accelerated and the heart palpitates. Nature has thus taken the trouble to provide its creatures the means of taking care of extra exertion.*

At the time when the connections of chemical and mechanical actions were unknown, physiologists were not in a position to explain correctly these simple and well-known facts. To quote from Valentin (*Physiologie*, vol. 1, p. 576):

"A man who climbs a mountain breathes harder because in order to correct the change in the center of gravity of his body he must bend himself forward and in this way in his forward motion the activity of his breathing muscles encounters difficulty. For similar reasons

---

* In long continued and excessive exertion the increased metabolism can suffer a qualitative alteration and lead to a pathological condition. The septic appearances noticed, for example, in a deer chased to death can be explained in this way.

the respiration becomes more violent for a man who jumps about, dances, etc."

The error in this explanation is at once evident. When the body is at rest even in the most uncomfortable and inconvenient posture, no increased respiration takes place. In dancing, jumping, climbing up and down mountains, walking on a plane surface, climbing a flight of stairs there is no essential obstacle to the free activity of the lung muscles. However, the increased intake of air, the consumption of oxygen, the production of carbon dioxide, the need for combustibles (i.e., nutriment), all of which are evident when human work is performed, all these remain unexplained so long as only the increased exertion of respiration of the worker is kept in mind rather than the result of this respiration.

When the strengthening of the chemical process in the organism takes place free heat is thereby produced in increased quantity. The temperature of the body surface is increased and transpiration (e.g., perspiration) results. It is noteworthy, however, that the most active components of the body are accustomed to sweat least. Strong peasant girls, whose hands perspire freely when they knit, can carry out heavy labor in the fields without their hands and arms becoming moist. Moses referred to the formation of sweat on the head during human labor, the head which itself produces no perceptible mechanical energy: He has God say to Adam: "In the sweat of thy face shalt thou eat bread." [First law of thermodynamics—Ed. note.]

The ability of living tissue to transform chemical energy into mechanical energy is called technically *irritability*.

In order to secure the clearest insight into the nature of this organic quality we shall compare it with a property of certain inorganic materials, namely the ability of fluids to transform heat into mechanical energy through their ability to expand. To this end we must introduce briefly here some principles relating to the heat and motion relations of elastic fluids.

If to a gas under constant pressure a definite amount of heat x is communicated, a part of this heat goes to increase the temperature of the gas, and this part, which we call call y, persists as "free" heat. The other part becomes "latent" and enables the gas to do mechanical work z. We have then the equation

$$x = y+z.$$

If now, turning to a living muscle, we set the magnitude of the oxidation process taking place in the capillaries of the muscle or of the corresponding heat equal to x', the actually developed free heat equal to y' and the associated mechanical energy produced equal to z', we get again

$$x' = y'+z'.$$

According to the mathematical methods followed in mechanics the physical energy z or z' is represented by the product of the pressure or tension by the volume. [Mayer is not quite precise here: he means of course $\int p dV$. If p is constant, or the average pressure, and V is the change in volume, we have pV, etc.—Ed. note.] This pressure in the case of gases as well as for muscles is inversely proportional to the volume. [This holds only for isothermal processes, though Mayer does not say so—Ed. note.] The pressure of a gas varies inversely as the volume. This is the law of Boyle or Mariotte. The value of the tension in a muscle varies inversely as the increase in the contraction. This is Schwann's law.*

---

* We can represent the origin of the mechanical energy z or z' in this fashion: The expansion of a gas or the contraction of a muscle is analogous to the raising of weight P through a height h. The gas pressure is analogous to P and the volume to h, so that $z = Ph$. Since, however, during the change in volume of the gas or contraction in length of the muscle the pressure or tension is not the same throughout but usually decreases during the process, P must take a different value for every point in the height h. Hence one has to take for P its value at *one* point on the line representing the height h [Mayer seems to be suggesting taking an average, but does not say so—Ed. note.], or one could take the special case $h = 0$. Then the product also vanishes and $z = 0$. For this case in which $x = y$, the pressure is called the *static* pressure and this is the case to which the laws of Boyle and Schwann apply. [Mayer is definitely off here in his physics!—Ed. note.] In the case of a muscle we have $x' = y'$ and $z' = 0$ when the supply of arterial blood in the capillaries remains constant (as temperature in the case of a gas in this case Schwann's law is to be applied).

Since the elasticity of a gas and the irritability of a muscle are prop-erties which relate to the transformation of given forms of energy, so likewise the existence of these properties is tied to the existence of the corresponding forms of energy. Where there is nothing, obviously nothing can be transformed. Without heat there can be no elasticity; without chemical activity irritability is unthinkable.

The temperature at which elasticity vanishes is, other things being equal, different for different gases. This is the ground for the distinc-tion between the so-called permanent gases and vapors.

The existence of irritability is connected with the presence of capillary oxygen and carbon. The measure of the necessary quan-tity of physical energy or its possible minimum is, however, as in the case of gases, different for different muscle fibers. This provides the reason for the different soundness of body of different classes of animals.

With greater permanence of irritability animals can cultivate their body haleness with the absorption of a smaller quantity of oxygen, breath can be held a longer time without disadvantage and asphyxiated states lead only gradually to actual death. On the other hand, for animals with small permanent irritability, an uninterrupted absorption of oxygen is the absolute condition for muscular irritability, and the weakening of the chemical process leads rather quickly to asphyxia and death.

After death the muscles of the first category (i.e., large permanent irritability) are still for a considerable time in a state to contract vigorously. On the other hand, the efficiency of the non-permanent muscles drops suddenly at the moment of death and shortly disappears altogether.

The motion-producing equipment of the cold-blooded animals is analogous in general to the permanent gases, whereas that of the warm-blooded animals is analogous to vapors.

The period of time within which the muscles of a freshly killed ani-mal retain the ability to contract, or what may be called the duration of irritability, depends on two factors: the first is the permanence of the muscle in and for itself, and the second is the presence of material necessary for chemical action. Where the latter fails, the irritability vanishes even when it has the greatest permanence. On the other hand, if this material is present in abundance, without regard to permanence, irritability still persists.

It was pointed out earlier that by the combustion of 1 part by weight of carbon a load of 3,637,000 parts by weight can be raised 1 meter. The consumption necessary for an individual weak contraction must therefore cease to be a perceptible quantity. It is only through the summation of the individual expenditures that this consumption becomes more and more noticeable. Through repeated expenditures in general the duration of irritability is shortened, for the supply of oxygen and combustible material will be used up by the action. A permanently irritable muscle may be in a position to permit several strong expenditures after a large part of its capillary blood has been removed by water injection. However, it must necessarily be inferior in endurance to a non-injected muscle. The admission of atmospheric air and an amount of heat favoring chemical activity lengthens the duration of irritability, as may be readily understood. Decreasing irritability, however, is most strongly countered by injection of oxygen under the arm. Consequently when the irritability of the heart threatens to vanish through lack of chemical material, help may still be provided by transfusion. The incidental calculation cited previously gave the result that in a single strong contraction of the peroneal (leg) muscle about a quarter of the available capillary oxygen and 1/5000th part of the carbon are used up and transformed into mechanical energy. The same ratio must hold for the action of the heart. From these numbers we obtain at once the well-known practical thesis that the "life-giving principle" is contained in the blood corpuscles and not in the blood plasma.*

In reptiles the duration of irritability is on the average greater than it is in fishes. From this we must not, however, conclude immediately that the permanent irritability is greater in the one than in the other,

---

* The injurious consequences which quickly follow the injection of even a very small quantity of a different kind of blood corpuscles into the blood stream cannot be explained by this latter hypothesis.

since the duration in question is dependent at the same time on both the natural irritability and the disposable quantity of oxygen present in the capillaries.

The arterial blood and venous blood of reptiles are continually mixing. Many blood corpuscles travel repeatedly through the body capillaries without having taken up oxygen. We conclude from this that the blood corpuscles of reptiles are destined to give up their oxygen only gradually to the body and that they retain this oxygen more firmly than the blood corpuscles of those classes of animals in which no mixing of arterial and venous blood takes place. Reptiles are therefore forced, in part at any rate, by their very living conditions to go a rather long time without the take up of oxygen. When they are subjected to nonrespirable kinds of gas like hydrogen and nitrogen they continue for quite a long time to form carbon dioxide. If we take into consideration the fact that oxygen is presented to reptiles in much more concentrated form than it is to fishes, we reach the conclusion that the blood corpuscles of reptiles in their physiological relations are different from the blood corpuscles of fishes in two ways: (1) through a stronger charging with oxygen in the capillaries of the organ of respiration, and (2) through a successive discharge of oxygen into the capillaries of the body.

The larger a blood corpuscle is, the greater the amount of oxygen it can absorb and retain. From this there results a simple relation between the physiological performance of the blood corpuscles and their volume ratios. We must at the same time recognize in the size of these corpuscles a significant influence on the duration of irritability. Indeed the largest blood corpuscles and the longest duration of irritability are found in the naked amphibians. The medium sized corpuscles and medium duration of irritability are found among the amphibians covered with scales, whereas the smallest blood corpuscles and the shortest irritability times are found in the cold-blooded vertebrates, the fishes.

It was said earlier that in a good steam engine about one-twentieth of the heat of combustion of the fuel can be transformed into mechanical energy. The corresponding figure for an explosive piece of ordnance is one-tenth, whereas it is one-fifth for a mammal.* We now ask, how great a fraction of the energy expended by a muscle is transformed into actual mechanical work? Suppose the muscle energy is x' and the mechanical work is z'. We are asking how great is z'/x', or to put it in words, how great is the mechanical efficiency of the muscle? The greater this ratio or efficiency or the more nearly it approximates unity, the more economically the muscle works.

Because of the lack of experimental measurements whose performance in this field is associated with almost insuperable difficulties, we must content ourselves with plausibilities and probabilities. Summarizing these briefly we arrive at the following general results: (1) the stronger the chemical activity in an animal or the stronger its carbon dioxide production, the smaller is the mechanical efficiency and the smaller is the production of mechanical energy in comparison with the production of heat; (2) through the analogy with elastic fluids, the mechanical efficiency is greatest in the permanently irritable muscles.

From these we are led to the following relations for vertebrates:

Carbon dioxide formation is the greatest and mechanical efficiency and permanence (persistence) of irritability least for birds.

Carbon dioxide production is somewhat weaker and mechanical efficiency and irritability persistence somewhat greater for mammals.

Carbon dioxide formation is small, mechanical efficiency and persistence large in the case of reptiles.

The smallest carbon dioxide formation and largest efficiency and persistence hold for the fishes.[†]

Chemical activity in the fetus is much weaker than in the newborn

* In these examples the heats of combustion of coal and charcoal were taken to be equal to that of carbon.

† Among the vertebrates for equal body size the warm-blooded variety obviously exhibit the largest persistent ability to expend mechanical energy. This was Nature's definite aim involving the sacrifice of economic considerations, for the warm-blooded animals need more combustible material than the cold-blooded ones in relation to their energy expenditure. The latter oxidize comparatively little. If richly fed they either increase in mass or they eliminate large quantities of combustible materials through the intestines and genito-urinary system. The steam engine is to be placed along side the warm-blooded animal. It has large capacity for transforming heat into mechanical energy but small mechanical efficiency. Whether technology will succeed in constructing "cold-blooded" engines which at the same time can do a great deal of work is to be doubted on physiological grounds.

infant. This follows at once from the observed fact of the lack of difference in color of the two blood varieties in the fetus. The production of mechanical energy through the heart and voluntary muscles is, on the other hand, approximately the same before and after birth. It follows from this that the mechanical efficiency before birth must be much greater than that after birth. The irritability persistence ends abruptly with birth. The prognosis in states of asphyxiation is hence very different as between children born breathing and those not breathing. Accordingly we may say:

The chemical activity is small, the mean mechanical efficiency and persistence of irritability large in the fetus.

The chemical activity is large and the mean efficiency and persistence small in the newly born.

If the parallel drawn between the elasticity of gases and the irritability of muscles is pushed further it encounters the fate of all analogies. The comparison which seems natural at first soon becomes an artificial one and gets lost at last in paradoxes. Gases are formless substances; muscles, however, are organized and their actions depend more or less on the influence of the motor nerves. This specific influence to which there is nothing corresponding in the case of expansible gases is called *innervation*.

Innervation, irritability and the chemical process are the three factors controlling muscle activity. The first has its anatomical seat in the brain and nerve medulla, the second in the primitive muscle fibers, and the third in the blood capillaries.

The action of the muscle, that is the transformation of chemical energy into mechanical energy, is conditioned in some mysterious way by a contact influence (catalysis) which experience indicates is associated with the nerve system. In so far as the equipment for animal motion is dependent on this influence in different degrees it is divided into two classes—the voluntary and involuntary. If we think of a steam engine in which one part does work as soon as steam is introduced, whereas the other part is set in motion only at the bidding and arrangement of the engineer, we have here an example of voluntary and involuntary motion apparatus. The engineer may make his influence felt on the apparatus available to him only with the expenditure of a certain amount of energy. This energy, however, is vanishingly small compared with the total energy developed by the apparatus and with increasing perfection of the device can be made smaller than any assigned quantity. [Mayer seems to have grasped the notion of control of energy transformation—cybernetics—Ed. note.] At the same time we must not accept it as possible nor even as probable that innervation can exercise its control over muscular activity without a noticeable expenditure of physical energy, without an electric current and without some kind of chemical activity.

Certain changes in innervation and chemical activity evidently correspond to observed fatigue and exhaustion.

As soon as the energy expenditure becomes too great in comparison with the given chemical–physical activity, local or complete exhaustion must ensue. If after discontinuance of energy expenditure the materials necessary for the chemical process are again made available, restoration of the energy-expending capacity follows. To a certain degree this can even happen in a dead muscle.

The physiological dogma of a consumption of irritability in a muscle through its action rests on an error. The inexhaustible activity of the most important muscles in the animal economy must be considered as an exception to the principle. A general law subject to such an exception must rest on a weak foundation.

As long as chemical activity proceeds in adequate fashion there is no built-in necessity for the muscle to be limited in its activity. If the muscles of a strong individual are moderately vigorously excited and there exists no lack of atmospheric oxygen and combustible material (i.e., food); even with continuous work there is no change in irritability.

Sleep, from whose dominion the sensorium (organs of sense) cannot break loose, stops at last the innervation and so puts a limit to the voluntary production of mechanical energy. The muscles and the nerves, however, do not sleep. The muscles serving the will can carry out motions even in the deepest sleep. A satisfactory meal and the rest needed for the production of blood can bring greater refreshment to one fatigued with vigorous exertion than a quiet sleep on an empty stomach. Horses while standing can restore their exhausted strength. Rich nourishment serves them better than upholstered resting places.

The cetaceans (whales) continue their swimming even during sleep, and birds of passage like sleep walkers can follow their path in part instinctively. On every part of the ocean surface one can see birds (especially swallows). These animals can complete in uninterrupted fashion stretches of over a thousand miles.*

Exhaustion takes place when after continued exertion and consumption no appropriate replacement is available, or if through too great exertion the chemical process is overwhelmed by the physiological activity. In this case we always have to do with an absolute or relative excess of production of mechanical energy.

However, there are also exertions with which no mechanical energy expenditure is involved, and these have no relation to chemical processes or to the blood.

Exertion is not to be confused with the expenditure of energy. For the expenditure of energy it is essential that the individual really lift his own weight or an outside weight up in the air or propel a mass in forward motion. The magnitude of the energy expenditure is measured by the load multiplied by the height through which it is raised or through the kinetic energy gained by the projected mass. The energy expenditure of a man who with great exertion holds up a motionless weight or merely stands motionless himself for hours on end is equal to zero. A wooden figure could indeed accomplish the same.†

* We must not fancy that the birds on the open sea follow a prescribed course, like the schools of dolphins and the ships themselves which follow the shortest course. These birds behave on the sea as they do on land, crisscrossing territory in every direction.

† On the subject of the quantity of mechanical energy expenditure people have been subject to great illusions. Conjurers know how to utilize this situation in order through their cleverness to give the impression of the great (expenditure of energy). In the consideration of states of disease one can easily be led into error by those who arouse fear in concluding that great mechanical energy is being expended, when practically none is involved. The development of energy in states of delirium is never so significant as in the case of vigorous physiological activity. The total effect which an epileptic can produce during a seizure can only be very small. The energy expenditure of the masseter muscle in lockjaw is zero, and the same is true of the whole muscular system in *rigor mortis*.

143

The fatigue or exhaustion in the case just discussed would appear to result from the continuous pressure on the nervous system. The sensation connected with this is not dissimilar to the so-called "going to sleep" of one's limbs. The workman Coulombs refused on one occasion to climb up and down stairs all day while unloaded. A discharge of the nerves is involved in this psychical act, which we can subsume under the concept of consciousness. The nerves remind the individual to refrain from unsuitable undertakings. In order to keep a weight freely floating in air neither an animal organism nor a steam engine is the suitable instrument. The best thing here is to use a hemp rope. *Suum cuique*.

The painful fatigue which results in the absence of any significant mechanical energy expenditure is distinguished from the exhaustion associated with the actual consumption of material in two principal ways, in so far as one keeps in mind exclusively physiological considerations. Since the primitive nerve fibers do not intercommunicate with each other by anastomosis, nervous exhaustion, even in the most extreme form, remains strictly local. It is restricted without exception to the muscle groups on which a claim is being made. Exhaustion, on the other hand, when it is not produced by a purely transient excess energy expenditure, spreads itself uniformly over the whole muscle system. The arm which after a long period of being stretched out horizontally sinks down from weariness, is able immediately thereafter to flex itself vigorously. The resting arm on the other side does not feel the fatigue at all. On the other hand, after a strenuous walk neither the arms nor the feet are disposed to make further energy expenditure. Since, moreover, in exertion without energy expenditure no consumption of material takes place, fatigue *sine materie* even in high degree in no way excludes the ability to expend mechanical energy. Thus the scholar who, against all the rules of dietetics, spends the whole day at his desk and gets himself tired there, in order to recover himself in the evening can climb a nearby mountain. On the other hand, exhaustion that takes place *cum materie* cancels out the ability to expend mechanical energy. For the restoration of the latter ability the intake of appropriate materials (food) is necessary. Hunger which results in consequence of the doing of work depends on the magnitude of the mechanical energy expended and not on the degree of exertion in and for itself. Correspondingly the consumption of oxygen is increased only through actual mechanical energy expenditure.*

In fatigue one must consider, in addition to the blood and the nerves, the cohesion conditions of the muscular and fibrous parts of the body. Through too heavy loading and stretching of the fibers, the motor apparatus is disturbed in its activity and through this a special kind of fatigue is introduced, which is not removed in a short time interval, not even with rest or the taking of sustenance. This actually becomes more noticeable during the rest period and like pain in the hip lessens again through motion. In this category belongs the pain due to stretching which one experiences, for example, in the femoral muscle if on the day previously one has quickly climbed down from a steep height. In the most extreme forms the stretching of the fibers represents surgical disease forms such as twisting of limbs, sprains and dislocations.

The different forces which are able to act as obstacles to the activity of healthy motional equipment combine themselves in individual cases in a fashion subject to many alternatives. Here, as in every physiological and pathological process, the organic and the chemical, the solid and the fluid, the nerve and the blood all simultaneously play their role. The phenomena of life may be compared to wonderful music full of magnificent harmonies as well as stirring dissonances. It is only in the cooperation of all instruments that the genuine harmony lies. And it is only this harmony that life finds its place.

---

* During great exertion one is accustomed to hold one's breath in order to create from the thorax a strong support for the organs of motion. No increased consumption of nutrients is necessarily connected with this. In wood cutting, climbing stairs, etc., no one will consciously strive to hold his breath.

Celestial Dynamics

Editorial Preface

This is the third scientific paper of Mayer to be published. With the German title "Beiträge zur Dynamik des Himmels in populärer Darstellung", it was published by Verlag von Johann Ulrich Landherr in Heilbronn in 1848. It was an expanded version of a paper "Sur la production de la lumiere et de la chaleur du soleil" which Mayer dispatched to the Academy of Sciences in Paris, but which was never acknowledged. The article was reprinted in Jacob J. Weyrauch's collection of Mayer's writings already referred to: Vol. 1, *Die Mechanik der Wärme*.

An English translation prepared by H. Debus appeared in *The Correlation and Conservation of Forces* (ed. by E. L. Youmans), D. Appleton and Co., New York, 1886, p. 259.

The following translation is that of H. Debus. A critique of the paper will be found in Part II.

I. Introduction

Every incandescent and luminous body diminishes in temperature and luminosity in the same degree as it radiates light and heat, and at last, provided its loss be not repaired from some other source of these agencies, becomes cold and non-luminous.

·For light, like sound, consists of vibrations which are communicated by the luminous or sounding body to a surrounding medium. It is perfectly clear that a body can only excite such vibrations in another substance when its own particles undergo a similar movement; for there is no cause for undulatory motion when a body is in a state of rest, or in a state of equilibrium with the medium by which it is surrounded. If a bell or a string is to be sounded, an external force must be applied; and this is the cause of the sound.

If the vibratory motion of a string could take place without any resistance, it would vibrate for all time; but in this case no sound could be produced, because sound is essentially the propagation of motion; and in the same degree as the string communicates its vibrations to the surrounding and resisting medium its own motion becomes weaker and weaker, until at last it sinks into a state of rest.

The sun has often and appropriately been compared to an incessantly sounding bell. But by what means is the power of this body kept up in undiminished force so as to enable him to send forth his rays into the universe in such a grand and magnificent manner? What are the causes which counteract or prevent his exhaustion, and thus save the planetary system from darkness and deadly cold?

Some endeavoured to approach "the grand secret," as Sir Wm. Herschel calls this question, by the assumption that the rays of the sun, being themselves perfectly cold, merely cause the "substance" of heat, supposed to be contained in bodies, to pass from a state of rest

148

into a state of motion, and that in order to send forth such cold rays the sun need not be a hot body, so that, in spite of the infinite development of light, the cooling of the sun was a matter not to be thought of.

It is plain that nothing is gained by such an explanation; for, not to speak of the hypothetical "substance" of heat, assumed to be at one time at rest and at another time in motion, now cold and then hot, it is a well-founded fact that the sun does not radiate a cold phosphorescent light, but a light capable of warming bodies intensely; and to ascribe such rays to a cold body is at once at variance with reason and experience.

Of course such and similar hypotheses could not satisfy the demands of exact science, and I will therefore try to explain in a more satisfactory manner than has been done up to this time the connexion between the sun's radiation and its effects. In doing so, I have to claim the indulgence of scientific men, who are acquainted with the difficulties of my task.

II. Sources of Heat

Before we turn our attention to the special subject of this paper, it will be necessary to consider the means by which light and heat are produced. Heat may be obtained from very different sources. Combustion, fermentation, putrefaction, slaking of lime, the decomposition of chloride of nitrogen and of gun-cotton, etc., are all of them sources of heat. The electric spark, the voltaic current, friction, percussion, and the vital processes are also accompanied by the evolution of this agent.

A general law of nature, which knows of no exception, is the following: In order to obtain heat, something must be expended; this something, however different it may be in other respects, can always be referred to one of two categories: either it consists of some material expended in a chemical process, or of some sort of mechanical work.

When substances endowed with considerable chemical affinity for each other combine chemically, much heat is developed during the process. We shall estimate the quantity of heat thus set free by the number of kilogrammes of water which it would heat 1 °C. The

149

quantity of heat necessary to raise 1 kilogramme of water 1 degree is called a unit of heat. [The kilocalorie.]

It has been established by numerous experiments that the combustion of 1 kilogramme of dry charcoal in oxygen, so as to form carbonic acid, yields 7200 units of heat, which fact may be briefly expressed by saying that charcoal furnishes 7200° degrees of heat.

Superior coal yields 6000°, perfectly dry wood from 3300° to 3900°, sulphur 2700°, and hydrogen 34,600° of heat.

According to experience, the number of units of heat only depends on the quantity of matter which is consumed, and not on the conditions under which the burning takes place. The same amount of heat is given out whether the combustion proceeds slowly or quickly, in atmospheric air or in pure oxygen gas. If in one case a metal be burnt in air and the amount of heat directly measured, and in another instance the same quantity of metal be oxidized in a galvanic battery, the heat being developed in some other place—say, the wire which conducts the current,—in both of these experiments the same quantity of heat will be observed.

The same law also holds good for the production of heat by mechanical means. The amount of heat obtained is only dependent on the quantity of power consumed, and is quite independent of the manner in which this power has been expended. If, therefore, the amount of heat which is produced by certain mechanical work is known, the quantity which will be obtained by any other amount of mechanical work can easily be found by calculation. It is of no consequence whether this work consists in the compression, percussion, or friction of bodies.

The amount of mechanical work done by a force may be expressed by a weight, and the height to which this weight would be raised by the same force. The mathematical expression for "work done", that is to say, a measure for this work, is obtained by multiplying the height expressed in feet or other units by the number of pounds or kilogrammes lifted to this height.

We shall take 1 kilogramme as the unit of weight, and 1 metre as the unit of height, and we thus obtain the weight of 1 kilogramme raised to the height of 1 metre as a unit measure of mechanical work performed. This measure we shall call a kilogrammetre, and adopt for it the symbol Km.

Mechanical work may likewise be measured by the velocity obtained by a given weight in passing from a state of rest into that of motion. The work done is then expressed by the product obtained by the multiplication of the weight by the square of its velocity. The first method, however, because it is the more convenient, is the one usually adopted; and the numbers obtained therefrom may easily be expressed in other units.

The product resulting from the multiplication of the number of units of weight and measures of height, or, as it is called, the product of mass and height, as well as the product of the mass and the square of its velocity, are called "*vis viva* of motion", "mechanical effect", "dynamical effect", "work done", "*quantité de travail*", etc.

The amount of mechanical work necessary for the heating of 1 kilogramme of water 1 °C has been determined by experiment to be = 367 Km; therefore Km = 0.00273 units of heat.*

A mass which has fallen through a height of 367 metres possesses a velocity of 84.8 metres in 1 second; a mass, therefore, moving with this velocity originates 1 °C of heat when its motion is lost by percussion, friction, etc. If the velocity be two or three times as great, 4° or 9° of heat will be developed. Generally speaking, when the velocity is c metres, the corresponding development of heat will be expressed by the formula

$$0.000139° \times c^2.$$

---

* This essay was published in 1848. At that time de la Roche and Berard's determination of the specific heat of air was generally accepted. If the physical constants used by Mayer be corrected according to the results of more recent investigation, the mechanical equivalent of heat is found to be 771.4 foot-pounds. Mr. Joule finds it = 772 foot-pounds.—Tr. note.

III. Measure of the Sun's Heat

The actinometer is an instrument invented by Sir John Herschel for the purpose of measuring the heating effect produced by the sun's rays. It is essentially a thermometer with a large cylindrical bulb filled with a blue liquid, which is acted upon by the sun's rays, and the expansion of which is measured by a graduated scale.

From observations made with this instrument, Sir John Herschel calculates the amount of heat received from the sun to be sufficient to melt annually at the surface of the globe a crust of ice 29.2 metres in thickness.

Pouillet has recently shown by some careful experiments with the lens pyrheliometer, an instrument invented by himself, that every square centimetre of the surface of our globe receives, on an average, in 1 minute an amount of solar heat which would raise the temperature of 1 gramme of water 0.4408°. Not much more than one-half of this quantity of heat, however, reaches the solid surface of our globe, since a considerable portion of it is absorbed by our atmosphere. The layer of ice which, according to Pouillet, could be melted by the solar heat which yearly reaches our globe would have a thickness of 30.89 metres.

A square metre of our earth's surface receives, therefore, according to Pouillet's results, which we shall adopt in the following pages, on an average in 1 minute 4.408 units of heat. The whole surface of the earth is = 9,260,500 geographical square miles*; consequently the earth receives in 1 minute 2247 billions of units of heat from the sun.

In order to obtain smaller numbers, we shall call the quantity of heat necessary to raise a cubic mile of water 1° C in temperature, a cubic mile of heat. Since 1 cubic mile of water weighs 408.54 billions of kilogrammes, a cubic mile of heat contains 408.54 billions of units of heat. The effect produced by the rays of the sun on the surface of the earth in 1 minute is therefore 5.5 cubic miles of heat.

Let us imagine the sun to be surrounded by a hollow sphere whose

---

* The geographical mile = 7420 metres, and one English mile = 1608 metres.

radius is equal to the mean distance of the earth from the sun, or 20,589,000 geographical miles; the surface of this sphere would be equal to 5326 billions of square miles. The surface obtained by the intersection of this hollow sphere and our globe, or the base of the cone of solar light which reaches our earth, stands to the whole surface of this hollow sphere as $\frac{9,260,500}{4}$: 5326 billions, or as 1 to 2300 millions. This is the ratio of the heat received by our globe to the whole amount of heat sent forth from the sun, which latter in one minute amounts to 12,650 millions of cubic miles of heat.

This amazing radiation ought, unless the loss is by some means made good, to cool considerably even a body of the magnitude of the sun.

If we assume the sun to be endowed with the same capacity for heat as a mass of water of the same volume, and its loss of heat by radiation to affect uniformly its whole mass, the temperature of the sun ought to decrease 1.8 °C yearly, and for the historic time of 5000 years this loss would consequently amount to 9000 °C.

A uniform cooling of the whole of the sun's huge mass cannot, however, take place; on the contrary, if the radiation were to occur at the expense of a given store of heat or radiant power, the sun would become covered in a short space of time with a cold crust, whereby radiation would be brought to an end. Considering the continued activity of the sun through countless centuries, we may assume with mathematical certainty the existence of some compensating influence to make good its enormous loss.

Is this restoring agency a chemical process?

If such were the case, the most favourable assumption would be to suppose the whole mass of the sun to be one lump of coal, the combustion of every kilogramme of which produces 6000 units of heat. Then the sun would only be able to sustain for forty-six centuries its present expenditure of light and heat, not to mention the oxygen necessary to keep up such an immense combustion, and other unfavourable circumstances.

The revolution of the sun on his axis has been suggested as the cause of his radiating energy. A closer examination proves this hypothesis also to be untenable.

Rapid rotation, without friction or resistance, cannot in itself alone be regarded as a cause of light and heat, especially as the sun is in no way to be distinguished from the other bodies of our system by velocity of axial rotation. The sun turns on his axis in about 25 days, and his diameter is nearly 112 times as great as that of the earth, from which it follows that a point on the solar equator travels but a little more than four times as quickly as a point on the earth's equator. The largest planet of the solar system, whose diameter is about $\frac{1}{10}$th that of the sun, turns on its axis in less than 10 hours; a point on its equator revolves about six times quicker than one on the solar equator. The outer ring of Saturn exceeds the sun's equator more than ten times in velocity of rotation. Nevertheless no generation of light or heat is observed on our globe, on Jupiter, or on the ring of Saturn.

It might be thought that friction, though undeveloped in the case of the other celestial bodies, might be engendered by the sun's rotation, and that such friction might generate enormous quantities of heat. But for the production of friction two bodies, at least, are always necessary which are in immediate contact with one another, and which move with different velocities or in different directions. Friction, moreover has a tendency to produce equal motion of the two rubbing bodies; and when this is attained, the generation of heat ceases. If now the sun be the one moving body, where is the other? and if the second body exist, what power prevents it from assuming the same rotary motion as the sun?

But could even these difficulties be disregarded, a weightier and more formidable obstacle opposes this hypothesis. The known volume and mass of the sun allow us to calculate the *vis viva* which he possesses in consequence of his rotation. Assuming his density to be uniform throughout his mass, and his period of rotation 25 days, it is equal to 182,300 quintillions of kilogrammetres (Km). But for one unit of heat generated, 367 Km are consumed; consequently the whole rotation-effect of the sun could only cover the expenditure of heat for the space of 183 years.

The space of our solar system is filled with a great number of ponderable objects, which have a tendency to move towards the centre of gravity of the sun; and in so doing, their rate of motion is more and more accelerated.

A mass, without motion, placed within the sphere of the sun's attraction, will obey this attraction, and, if there be no disturbing influences, will fall in a straight line into the sun. In reality, however, such a rectilinear path can scarcely occur, as may be shown by experiment.

Let a weight be suspended by a string so that it can only touch the floor in one point. Lift the weight up to a certain height, and at the same time stretch the string out to its full length; if the weight be now allowed to fall, it will be observed, almost in every case, not to reach at once the point on the floor towards which it tends to move, but to move round this point for some time in a curved line.

The reason of this phenomenon is that the slightest deviation of the weight from its shortest route towards the point on the floor, caused by some disturbing influence such as the resistance of the air against a not perfectly uniform surface, will maintain itself as long as motion lasts. It is nevertheless possible for the weight to move at once to the point; the probability of its doing so, however, becomes the less as the height from which it is allowed to drop increases, or the string, by means of which it is suspended, is lengthened.

Similar laws influence the movements of bodies in the space of the solar system. The height of the fall is here represented by the original distance from the sun which the body begins to move; the length of the string by the sun's attraction, which increases when the distance decreases; and the small surface of contact on the floor by the area of the section of the sun's sphere. If now a cosmical mass within the physical limits of the sun's sphere of attraction begins its fall toward that heavenly body, it will be disturbed in its long path for many centuries, at first by the nearest fixed stars, and afterwards by the bodies of the solar system. Motion of such a mass in a straight line, or its perpendicular fall into the sun, would, therefore, under such conditions, be impossible. The observed movement of all planetary bodies in closed curves agrees with this.

We shall now return to the example of the weight suspended by a string and oscillating round a point towards which it is attracted. The diameters of the orbits described by this weight are observed to be nearly equal; continued observation, however, shows that these diameters gradually diminish in length, so that the weight will by degrees approach the point in which it can touch the floor. The weight, however, touches the floor not in a mathematical point, but in a small surface; as soon, therefore, as the diameter of the curve in which the weight moves is equal to the diameter of this surface, the weight will touch the floor. This final contact is no accidental or improbable event, but a necessary phenomenon caused by the resistance which the oscillating mass constantly suffers from the air and friction. If all resistance could be annihilated, the motion of the weight would of course continue in equal oscillations.

The same law holds good for celestial bodies.

The movements of celestial bodies in an absolute vacuum would be as uniform as those of a mathematical pendulum, whereas a resisting medium pervading all space would cause the planets to move in shorter and shorter orbits, and at last to fall into the sun.

Assuming such a resisting medium, these wandering celestial bodies must have on the periphery of the solar system their cradle, and in its centre their grave; and however long the duration, and however great the number of their revolutions may be, as many masses will on the average in a certain time arrive at the sun as formerly in a like period of time came within his sphere of attraction.

All these bodies plunge with a violent impetus into their common grave. Since no cause exists without an effect, each of these cosmical masses will, like a weight falling to the earth, produce by its percussion an amount of heat proportional to its *vis viva*.

From the idea of a sun whose attraction acts throughout space, of ponderable bodies scattered throughout the universe, and of a resisting æther, another idea necessarily follows—that, namely, of a continual and inexhaustible generation of heat on the central body of this cosmical system.

Whether such a conception be realized in our solar system—whether, in other words, the wonderful and permanent evolution of light and

156

heat be caused by the uninterrupted fall of cosmical matter into the sun—will now be more closely examined.

The existence of matter in a primordial condition (*Urmaterie*), moving about in the universe, and assumed to follow the attraction of the nearest stellar system, will scarcely be denied by astronomers and physicist; for the richness of surrounding nature, as well as the aspect of the starry heavens, prevents the belief that the wide space which separates our solar system from the regions governed by the other fixed stars is a vacant solitude destitute of matter. We shall leave, however, all suppositions concerning subjects so distant from us both in time and space, and confine our attention exclusively to what may be learnt from the observation of the existing state of things.

Besides the fourteen known planets with their eighteen satellites, a great many other cosmical masses move within the space of the planetary system, of which the comets deserve to be mentioned first.

Kepler's celebrated statement that "there are more comets in the heavens than fish in the ocean", is founded on the fact that, of all the comets belonging to our solar system, comparatively few can be seen by the inhabitants of the earth, and therefore the not inconsiderable number of actually observed comets obliges us, according to the rules of the calculus of probabilities, to assume the existence of a great many more beyond the sphere of our vision.

Besides planets, satellites, and comets, another class of celestial bodies exists within our solar system. These are masses which, on account of their smallness, may be considered as cosmical atoms, and which Arago has appropriately called asteroids. They, like the planets and the comets, are governed by gravity, and move in elliptical orbits round the sun. When accident brings them into the immediate neighbourhood of the earth, they produce the phenomena of shooting-stars and fireballs.

It has been shown by repeated observation, that on a bright night 20 minutes seldom elapse without a shooting-star being visible to an observer in any situation. At certain times these meteors are observed in astonishingly great numbers; during the meteoric shower at Boston, which lasted nine hours, when they were said to fall "crowded together like snow-flakes", they were estimated as at least 240,000. On the whole, the number of asteroids which come near the earth in the space of a year must be computed to be many thousands of millions. This, without doubt, is only a small fraction of the number of asteroids that move round the sun, which number, according to the rules of the calculus of probabilities, approaches the infinite.

As has been already stated, on the existence of a resisting æther it depends whether the celestial bodies, the planets, the comets, and the asteroids move at constant mean distances round the sun, or whether they are constantly approaching that central body.

Scientific men do not doubt the existence of such an æther. Littrow, amongst others, expresses himself on this point as follows:

"The assumption that the planets and the comets move in an absolute vacuum can in no way be admitted. Even if the space between celestial bodies contained no other matter than that necessary for the existence of light (whether light be considered as emission of matter or the undulations of a universal æther), this alone is sufficient to alter the motion of the planets in the course of time and the arrangement of the whole system itself; the fall of all the planets and the comets into the sun and the destruction of the present state of the solar system must be the final results of this action."

A direct proof of the existence of such a resisting medium has been furnished by the academician Encke. He found that the comet named after him, which revolves round the sun in the short space of 1207 days, shows a regular acceleration of its motion, in consequence of which the time of each revolution is shortened by about 6 hours.

From the great density and magnitude of the planets, the shortening of the diameters of their orbits proceeds, as might be expected, very slowly, and is up to the present time inappreciable. The smaller the cosmical masses are, on the contrary, other circumstances remaining the same, the faster they move towards the sun; it may therefore happen that in a space of time wherein the mean distance of the earth from the sun would diminish 1 metre, a small asteroid would travel more than one thousand miles towards the central body.

As cosmical masses stream from all sides in immense numbers towards the sun, it follows that they must become more and more crowded together as they approach thereto. The conjecture at once suggests itself that the zodiacal light, the nebulous light of vast dimensions which surrounds the sun, owes its origin to such closely-packed asteroids. However it may be, this much is certain, that this phenomenon is caused by matter which moves according to the same laws as the planets round the sun, and it consequently follows that the whole mass which originates the zodiacal light is continually approaching the sun and falling into it.

This light does not surround the sun uniformly on all sides; that is to say, it has not the form of a sphere, but that of a thin convex lens, the greater diameter of which is in the plane of the solar equator, and accordingly it has to an observer on our globe a pyramidal form. Such lenticular distribution of the masses in the universe is repeated in a remarkable manner in the disposition of the planets and the fixed stars.

From the great number of cometary masses and asteroids and the zodiacal light on the one hand, and the existence of a resisting aether on the other, it necessarily follows that ponderable matter must continually be arriving on the solar surface. The effect produced by these masses evidently depends on their final velocity; and, in order to determine the latter, we shall discuss some of the elements of the theory of gravitation.

The final velocity of a weight attracted by and moving towards a celestial body will become greater as the height through which the weight falls increases. This velocity, however, if it be only produced by the fall, cannot exceed a certain magnitude; it has a maximum, the value of which depends on the volume and mass of the attracting celestial body.

Let r be the radius of a spherical and solid celestial body and g the velocity at the end of the first second of a weight falling on the surface of this body; then the greatest velocity which this weight can obtain by its fall towards the celestial body, or the velocity with which it will

159

arrive at its surface after a fall from an infinite height, is $\sqrt{2gr}$ in 1 second. This number, wherein g and r are expressed in metres, we shall call G.

For our globe the value of g is 9.8164 ... and that of r 6,369,800; and consequently on our earth

$$G = \sqrt{(2 \times 9.8164 \times 6,369,800)} = 11,183.$$

The solar radius is 112.05 times that of the earth, and the velocity produced by gravity on the sun's surface is 28.36 times greater than the same velocity on the surface of our globe; the greatest velocity therefore which a body could obtain in consequence of the solar attraction, or

$$G = \sqrt{(28.36 \times 112.05)} \times 11,183 = 630,400;$$

that is, this maximum velocity is equal to 630,400 metres, or 85 geographical miles in 1 second.

By the help of this constant number, which may be called the *characteristic* of the solar system, the velocity of a body in central motion may easily be determined at any point of its orbit. Let a be the mean distance of the planetary body from the centre of gravity of the sun, or the greater semidiameter of its orbit (the radius of the sun being taken as unity); and let h be the distance of the same body at any point of its orbit from the centre of gravity of the sun; then the velocity, expressed in metres, of the planet at the distance h is

$$G \times \sqrt{\frac{2a-h}{2a \times h}}.$$

At the moment the planet comes in contact with the solar surface, h is equal to 1, and its velocity is therefore

$$G \times \sqrt{\frac{2a-1}{2a}}.$$

It follows from this formula that the smaller $2a$ (or the major axis of the orbit of a planetary body) becomes, the less will be its velocity when it reaches the sun. This velocity, like the major axis, has a minimum; for so long as the planet moves outside the sun, its major axis cannot be shorter than the diameter of the sun, or, taking the solar radius as a unit, the quantity $2a$ can never be less than 2. The smallest velocity with which we can imagine a cosmical body to arrive on the surface of the sun is consequently

$$G \times \sqrt{\frac{1}{2}} = 445,750,$$

or a velocity of 60 geographical miles in 1 second.

For this smallest value the orbit of the asteroid is circular; for a larger value it becomes elliptical, until finally, with increasing excentricity, when the value of $2a$ approaches infinity, the orbit becomes a parabola. In the last case the velocity is

$$G \times \sqrt{\frac{\infty - 1}{\infty}} = G,$$

or, 85 geographical miles in 1 second.

If the value of the major axis become negative, or the orbit assume the form of a hyperbola, the velocity may increase without end. But this could only happen when cosmical masses enter the space of the solar system with a projected velocity, or when masses, having missed the sun's surface, move into the universe and never return; hence a velocity greater than G can only be regarded as a rare exception, and we shall therefore only consider velocities comprised within the limits of 60 and 80 miles.*

The final velocity with which a weight moving in a straight line towards the centre of the sun arrives at the solar surface is expressed by the formula

$$c = G \times \sqrt{\frac{h - 1}{h}},$$

wherein c expresses the final velocity in metres, and h the original

---

* The relative velocity also with which an asteroid reaches the solar surface depends in some degree on the velocity of the sun's rotation. This, however, as well as the rotatory effect of the asteroid, is without moment, and may be neglected.

distance from the centre of the sun in terms of solar radius. If this formula be compared with the foregoing, it will be seen that a mass which, after moving in central motion, arrives at the sun's surface has the same velocity as it would possess had it fallen perpendicularly into the sun from a distance* equal to the major axis of its orbit; whence it is apparent that a planet, on arriving at the sun, moves at least as quickly as a weight which falls freely towards the sun from a distance as great as the solar radius, or 96,000 geographical miles.

What thermal effect corresponds to such velocities? Is the effect sufficiently great to play an important part in the immense development of heat on the sun?

This crucial question may be easily answered by help of the preceding considerations. According to the formula given at the end of Section II, the degree of heat generated by percussion is

$$= 0.000139° \times c^2,$$

where c denotes the velocity of the striking body expressed in metres. The velocity of an asteroid when it strikes the sun measures from 445,750 to 630,400 metres; the caloric effect of the percussion is consequently equal to from $27\frac{1}{2}$ to 55 millions of degrees of heat.[†]

An asteroid, therefore, by its fall into the sun developes from 4600 to 9200 times as much heat as would be generated by the combustion of an equal mass of coal.

IV. Origin of the Sun's Heat

The question why the planets move in curved orbits, one of the grandest of problems, was solved by Newton in consequence, it is believed, of his reflecting on the fall of an apple. This story is not improbable, for we are on the right track for the discovery of truth when once we clearly recognize that between great and small no qualit-

---

* This distance is to be counted from the centre of the sun.

† Throughout this memoir the degrees of heat are expressed in the Centigrade scale. Unless stated to the contrary, the measures of length are given in geographical miles. A geographical mile = 7420 metres, and an English mile = 1608 metres.—Tr. note.

ative but only a quantitative difference exists—when we resist the suggestions of an ever active imagination, and look for the same laws in the greatest as well as in the smallest processes of nature.

This universal range is the essence of a law of nature, and the touchstone of the correctness of human theories. We observe the fall of an apple, and investigate the law which governs this phenomenon; for the earth we substitute the sun, and for the apple a planet, and thus possess ourselves of the key to the mechanics of the heavens.

As the same laws prevail in the greater as well as in the smaller processes of nature, Newton's method may be used in solving the problem of the origin of the sun's heat. We know the connexion between the space through which a body falls, the velocity, the *vis viva*, and the generation of heat on the surface of this globe; if we again substitute for the earth the sun, with a mass 350,000 greater, and for a height of a few metres celestial distances, we obtain a generation of heat exceeding all terrestrial measures. And since we have sufficient reason to assume the actual existence of such mechanical processes in the heavens, we find therein the only tenable explanation of the origin of the heat of the sun.

The fact that the development of heat by mechanical means on the surface of our globe is, as a rule, not so great, and cannot be so great as the generation of the same agent by chemical means, as by combustion, follows from the laws already discussed; and this fact cannot be used as an argument against the assumption of a greater development of heat by a greater expenditure of mechanical work. It has been shown that the heat generated by a weight falling from a height of 367 metres is only $\frac{1}{6000}$th part of the heat produced by the combustion of the same weight of coal; just as small is the amount of heat developed by a weight moving with the not inconsiderable velocity of 85 metres in 1 second. But, according to the laws of mechanics, the effect is proportional to the square of the velocity; if therefore the weight move 100 times faster, or with a velocity of 8500 metres in 1 second, it will produce a greater effect than the combustion of an equal quantity of coal.

It is true that so great a velocity cannot be obtained by human means; everyday experience, however, shows the development of high degrees of temperature by mechanical processes.

In the common flint and steel, the particles of steel which are struck off are sufficiently heated to burn in air. A few blows directed by a skilful blacksmith with a sledge-hammer against a piece of cold metal may raise the temperature of the metal at the points of collision to redness.

The new crank of a steamer, whilst being polished by friction, becomes red-hot, several buckets of water being required to cool it down to its ordinary temperature.

When a railway train passes with even less than its ordinary velocity along a very sharp curve of the line, sparks are observed in consequence of the friction against the rails.

One of the grandest constructions for the production of motion by human art is the channel in which the wood was allowed to glide down from the steep and lofty sides of Mount Pilatus into the plain below. This wooden channel which was built about thirty years ago by the engineer Rupp, was 9 English miles in length; the largest trees were shot down it from the top to the bottom of the mountain in about $2\frac{1}{2}$ minutes. The momentum possessed by the trees on their escaping at their journey's end from the channel was sufficiently great to bury their thicker ends in the ground to the depth of from 6 to 8 metres. To prevent the wood getting too hot and taking fire, water was conducted in many places into the channel.

This stupendous mechanical process, when compared with cosmical processes on the sun, appears infinitely small. In the latter case it is the mass of the sun which attracts, and in lieu of the height of Mount Pilatus we have distances of a hundred thousand and more miles; the amount of heat generated by cosmical falls is therefore at least 9 million times greater than in our terrestrial example.

Rays of heat on passing through glass and other transparent bodies undergo partial absorption, which differs in degree, however, according to the temperature of the source from which the heat is derived. Heat radiated from sources less warm than boiling water is almost completely stopped by thin plates of glass. As the temperature of a source of heat increases, its rays pass more copiously through diathermic bodies. A plate of glass, for example, weakens the rays of a red-hot substance, even when the latter is placed very close to it, much more than it does those emanating at a much greater distance from a white-hot body. If the quality of the sun's rays be examined in this respect, their diathermic energy is found to be far superior to that of all artificial sources of heat. The temperature of the focus of a concave metallic reflector in which the sun's light has been collected is only diminished from one-seventh to one-eighth by the interposition of a screen of glass. If the same experiment be made with an artificial and luminous source of heat, it is found that, though the focus be very hot when the screen is away, the interposition of the latter cuts off nearly all the heat; moreover, the focus will not recover its former temperature when reflector and screen are placed sufficiently near to the source of heat to make the focus appear brighter than it did in the former position without the glass screen.

The empirical law, that the diathermic energy of heat increases with the temperature of the source from which the heat is radiated, teaches us that the sun's surface must be much hotter than the most powerful process of combustion could render it.

Other methods furnish the same conclusion. If we imagine the sun to be surrounded by a hollow sphere, it is clear that the inner surface of this sphere must receive all the heat radiated from the sun. At the distance of our globe from the sun, such a sphere would have a radius 215 times as great, and an area 46,000 times as large as the sun himself; those luminous and calorific rays, therefore, which meet this spherical surface at right angles retain only $\frac{1}{46,000}$th part of their original intensity. If it be further considered that our atmosphere absorbs a part of the solar rays, it is clear that the rays which reach the Tropics of our earth at noonday can only possess from $\frac{1}{50,000}$th to $\frac{1}{60,000}$th of the power with which they started. These rays, when gathered from a surface of from 5 to 6 square metres, and concentrated in an area of 1 square centimetre, would produce about the temperature which exists on the sun, a temperature more then sufficient to vaporize platinum, rhodium, and similar metals.

The radiation calculated in Section III likewise proves the enormous temperature of the solar surface. From the determination mentioned therein, it follows that each square centimetre of the sun's surface loses by radiation about 80 units of heat per minute—an immense quantity in comparison with terrestrial radiations.

A correct theory of the origin of the sun's heat must explain the cause of such enormous temperatures. This explanation can be deduced from the foregoing statements. According to Pouillet, the temperature at which bodies appear intensely white-hot is about 1500 °C. The heat generated by the combustion of 1 kilogramme of hydrogen is, as determined by Dulong, 34,500, and according to the more recent experiments of Grassi, 34,666 units of heat. One part of hydrogen combines with eight parts of oxygen to form water; hence 1 kilogramme of these two gases mixed in this ratio would produce 3850°.

Let us now compare this heat with the amount of the same agent generated by the fall of an asteroid into the sun. Without taking into account the low specific heat of such masses when compared with that of water, we find the heat developed by the asteroid to be from 7000 to 15,000 times greater than that of the oxyhydrogen mixture. From data like these, the extraordinary diathermic energy of the sun's rays, the immense radiation from his surface, and the high temperature in the focus of the reflector are easily accounted for.

The facts mentioned above show that, unless we assume on the sun the existence of matter with unheard of chemical properties as a *deus ex machinâ*, no chemical process could maintain the present high radiation of the sun; it also follows from the above results, that the chemical nature of bodies which fall into the sun does not in the least affect our conclusions; the effect produced by the most inflammable substance would not differ by one-thousandth part from that resulting from the fall of matter possessing but feeble chemical affinities. As the brightest artificial light appears dark in comparison with the sun's light, so the mechanical processes of the heavens throw into the shade the most powerful chemical actions.

The quality of the sun's rays, as dependent on his temperature, is of the greatest importance to mankind. If the solar heat were originated by a chemical process, and amounted near its source to a temperature of a few thousand degrees, it would be possible for the light to reach us, whilst the greater part of the more important calorific rays would be absorbed by the higher strata of our atmosphere and then returned to the universe.

In consequence of the high temperature of the sun, however, our atmosphere is highly diathermic to his rays, so that the latter reach the surface of our earth and warm it. The comparatively low temperature of the terrestrial surface is the cause why the heat cannot easily radiate back through the atmosphere into the universe. The atmosphere acts, therefore, like an envelope, which is easily pierced by the solar rays, but which offers considerable resistance to the radiant heat escaping from our earth; its action resembles that of a valve which allows liquid to pass freely in one, but stops the flow in the opposite direction.

The action of the atmosphere is of the greatest importance as regards climate and meteorological processes. It must raise the mean temperature of the earth's surface. After the setting of the sun—in fact, in all places where his rays do not reach the surface, the temperature of the earth would soon be as low as that of the universe, if the atmosphere were removed, or if it did not exist. Even the powerful solar rays in the tropics would be unable to preserve water in its liquid state.

Between the great cold which would reign at all times and in all places, and the moderate warmth which in reality exists on our globe, intermediate temperatures may be imagined; and it is easily seen that the mean temperature would decrease if the atmosphere were to become more and more rare. Such a rarefaction of a valve-like acting atmosphere actually takes place as we ascend higher and higher above the level of the sea, and it is accordingly and necessarily accompanied by a corresponding diminution of temperature.

This well-known fact of the lower mean temperature of places of greater altitude has led to the strangest hypotheses. The sun's rays were not supposed to contain all the conditions for warming a body, but to set in motion the "substance" of heat contained in the earth. This "substance" of heat, cold when at rest, was attracted by the earth, and was therefore found in greater abundance near the centre of the globe. This view, it was thought, explained why the warming power of the sun was so much weaker at the top of a mountain than at the bottom, and why, in spite of his immense radiation, he retained his full powers.

This belief, which especially prevails amongst imperfectly informed people, and which will scarcely succumb to correct views, is directly contradicted by the excellent experiments made by Pouillet at different altitudes with the pyrheliometer. These experiments show that, everything else being equal, the generation of heat by the solar rays is more powerful in higher altitudes than near the surface of our globe, and that consequently a portion of these rays is absorbed on their passage through the atmosphere. Why, in spite of this partial absorption, the mean temperature of low altitudes is nevertheless higher than it is in more elevated positions, is explained by the fact that the atmosphere stops to a far greater degree the calorific rays emanating from the earth than it does those from the sun.

V. Constancy of the Sun's Mass

Newton, as is well known, considered light to be the emission of luminous particles from the sun. In the continued emission of light this great philosopher saw a cause tending to diminish the solar mass; and he assumed, in order to make good this loss, comets and other cosmical masses to be continually falling into the central body.

If we express this view of Newton's in the language of the undulatory theory, which is now universally accepted, we obtain the results developed in the preceding pages. It is true that our theory does not accept a peculiar "substance" of light or of heat; nevertheless, according to it, the radiation of light and heat consists also in purely material processes, in a sort of motion, in the vibrations of ponderable resisting substances. Quiescence is darkness and death; motion is light and life.

An undulating motion proceeding from a point or a plane and excited in an unlimited medium, cannot be imagined apart from another simultaneous motion, a translation of the particles themselves;* it therefore follows, not only from the emission, but also from the undulatory theory, that radiation continually diminishes the mass of the sun. Why, nevertheless, the mass of the sun does not really diminish has already been stated.

The radiation of the sun is a centrifugal action equivalent to a centripetal motion.

The caloric effect of the centrifugal action of the sun can be found by direct observation; it amounts, according to Section III, in 1 minute to 12,650 millions of cubic miles of heat, or 5.17 quadrillions of units of heat. In Section IV it has been shown that 1 kilogramme of the mass of an asteroid originates from 27.5 to 55 millions of units of heat; the quantity of cosmical masses, therefore, which falls every minute into the sun amounts to from 94,000 to 188,000 billions of kilogrammes.

To obtain this remarkable result, we made use of a method which is common in physical inquiries. Observation of the moon's motion reveals to us the external form of the earth. The physicist determines with the torsion-balance the weight of a planet, just as the merchant finds the weight of a parcel of goods, whilst the pendulum has become a magic power in the hands of the geologist, enabling him to discover cavities in the bowels of the earth. Our case is similar to these. By observation and calculation of the velocity of sound in our atmosphere, we obtain the ratio of the specific heat of air under constant pressure and under constant volume, and by the help of this number we deterine the quantity of heat generated by mechanical work. The heat which arrives from the sun in a given time on a small surface of our globe serves as a basis for the calculation of the whole radiating effect of the sun; and the result of a series of observations and well-founded conclusions is the quantitative determination of those cosmical masses which the sun receives from the space through which he sends forth his rays.

Measured by terrestrial standards, the ascertained number of so

* This centrifugal motion is perhaps the cause of the repulsion of the tails on comets when in the neighbourhood of the sun, as observed by Bessel.

many billions of kilogrammes per minute appears incredible. This quantity, however, may be brought nearer to our comprehension by comparison with other cosmical magnitudes. The nearest celestial body to us (the moon) has a mass of about 90,000 trillions of kilogrammes, and it would therefore cover the expenditure of the sun for from 1 to 2 years. The mass of the earth would afford nourishment to the sun for a period of from 60 to 120 years.

To facilitate the appreciation of the masses and the distances occurring in the planetary system, Herschel draws the following picture. Let the sun be represented by a globe 1 metre in diameter. The nearest planet (Mercury) will be about as large as a pepper-corn, $3\frac{1}{4}$ millimetres in thickness, at a distance of 40 metres. 78 and 107 metres distant from the sun will move Venus and the Earth, each 9 millimetres in diameter, or a little larger than a pea. Not much more that a quarter of a metre from the Earth will be the Moon, the size of a mustard seed, $2\frac{1}{2}$ millimetres in diameter. Mars, at a distance of 160 metres, will have about half the diameter of the Earth; and the smaller planets (Vesta, Hebe, Astrea, Juno, Pallas, Ceres, &c.), at a distance of from 250 to 300 metres from the sun, will resemble particles of sand. Jupiter and Saturn, 560 and 1000 metres distant from the centre, will be represented by oranges, 10 and 9 centimetres in diameter. Uranus, of the size of a nut 4 centimetres across, will be 2000 metres; and Neptune, as large as an apple 6 centimetres in diameter, will be nearly twice as distant, or about half a geographical mile away from the sun. From Neptune to the nearest fixed star will be more than 2000 geographical miles.

To complete this picture, it is necessary to imagine finely divided matter grouped in a diversified manner, moving slowly and gradually towards the large central globe, and on its arrival attaching itself thereto; this matter, when favourably illuminated by the sun, represents itself to us as the zodiacal light. This nebulous substance forms also an important part of a creation in which nothing is by chance, but wherein all is arranged with Divine foresight and wisdom.

The surface of the sun measures 115,000 millions of square miles, or $6\frac{1}{3}$ trillions of square metres; the mass of matter which in the shape of asteroids falls into the sun every minute is from 94,000 to 188,000 billions of kilogrammes; 1 square metre of solar surface, therefore, receives on an average from 15 to 30 grammes of matter per minute.

To compare this process with a terrestrial phenomenon, a gentle rain may be considered which sends down in 1 hour a layer of water 1 milli- metre in thickness (during a thunderstorm the rainfall is often from ten to fifteen times this quantity), this amounts on a square metre to 17 grammes per minute.

The continual bombardment of the sun by these cosmical masses ought to increase its volume as well as its mass, if centripetal action only existed. The increase of volume, could scarcely be appreciated by man; for if the specific gravity of these cosmical masses be assumed to be the same as that of the sun, the enlargement of his apparent dia- meter to the extent of one second, the smallest appreciable magnitude, would require from 33,000 to 66,000 years.

Not quite so inappreciable would be the increase of the mass of the sun. If this mass, or the weight of the sun, were augmented, an accelera- tion of the motion of the planets in their orbits would be the consequ- ence, whereby their times of revolution round the central body would be shortened. The mass of the sun is 2.1 quintillions of kilogrammes; and the mass of the cosmical matter annually arriving at the sun stands to the above as 1 to from 21 to 42 millions. Such an augmentation of the weight of the sun ought to shorten the sidereal year from $\frac{1}{42,000,000}$th to $\frac{1}{85,000,000}$th of its length, or from $\frac{3}{4}$th to $\frac{3}{8}$ths of a second. The observations of astronomers do not agree with this conclusion; we must therefore fall back on the theory mentioned at the beginning of this Section, which assumes that the sun, like the ocean, is constantly losing and receiving equal quantities of matter. This harmonizes with the supposition that the *vis viva* of the universe is a constant quantity.

VI. The Spots on the Sun's Disc

The solar disc presents, according to Sir John Herschel, the following appearance.

"When the sun is observed through a powerful telescope provided with coloured glasses in order to lessen the heat and brightness which would be hurtful to the eyes, large dark spots are often seen surrounded by edges which are not quite so dark as the spots themselves, and which are called penumbrae. These spots, however, are neither permanent nor unchangeable. When observed from day to day, or even from hour to hour, their form is seen to change; they expand or contract, and finally disappear; on other parts of the solar surface new spots spring into existence where none could be discovered before. When they disappear, the darker part in the middle of the spot contracts to a point and vanishes sooner than the edge. Sometimes they break up into two or more parts that show all the signs of mobility characteristic of a liquid, and the extraordinary commotion which it seems only possible for gaseous matter to possess. The magnitude of their motion is very great. An arc of 1 second, as seen from our globe, corresponds to 465 English miles on the sun's disc; a circle of this diameter, which measures nearly 220,000 English square miles, is the smallest area that can be seen on the solar surface. Spots, however, more than 45,000 English miles in diameter, and, if we may trust some statements, of even greater dimensions, have been observed. For such a spot to disappear in the course of six weeks (and they rarely last longer), the edges, whilst approaching each other, must move through a space of more than 1000 miles per diem.

"That portion of the solar disc which is free from spots is by no means uniformly bright. Over it are scattered small dark spots or pores, which are found by careful observation to be in a state of continual change. The slow sinking of some chemical precipitates in a transparent liquid, when viewed from the upper surface and in a direction perpendicular thereto, resembles more accurately than any other phenomenon the changes which the pores undergo. The similarity is so striking, in fact, that one can scarcely resist the idea that the appearances above described are owing to a luminous medium moving about in a non-luminous atmosphere, either like the clouds in our air, or in wide-spread planes and flame-like columns, or in rays like the aurora borealis.

"Near large spots, or extensive groups of them, large spaces are observed to be covered with peculiarly marked lines much brighter than the other parts of the surface; these lines are curved, or deviate in branches, and are called faculae. Spots are often seen between these lines, or to originate there. These are in all probability the crests of immense waves in the luminous regions of the solar atmosphere, and bear witness to violent action in their immediate neighbourhood."

The changes on the solar surface evidently point to the action of some external disturbing force; for every moving power resident in the sun itself ought to exhaust itself by its own action. These changes, therefore, are no unimportant confirmation of the theory explained in these pages.

At the same time it must be observed that our knowledge of physical heliography is, from the nature of the subject, very limited; even the meteorological processes and other phenomena of our own planet are still in many respects enigmatical. For this reason no special information could be given about the manner in which the solar surface is affected by cosmical masses. However, I may be allowed to mention some probable conjectures which offer themselves.

The extraordinarily high temperature which exists on the sun almost precludes the possibility of its surface being solid; it doubtless consists of an uninterrupted ocean of fiery fluid matter. This gaseous envelope becomes more rarefied in those parts most distant from the sun's centre.

As most substances are able to assume the gaseous state of aggregation at high temperatures, the height of the sun's atmosphere cannot be inconsiderable. There are, however sound reasons for believing that the relative height of the solar atmosphere is not very great.

Since the gravity is 28 times greater on the sun's surface than it is on our earth, a column of air on the former must cause a pressure 28 times greater than it would on our globe. This great pressure compresses air as much as a temperature of 8000° would expand it.

In a still greater degree than this increased gravity do the qualities peculiar to gases affect the height of the solar atmosphere. In consequence of these properties, the density of our atmosphere rapidly diminishes as we ascend, and increases as we descend. Generally speaking, rarefaction increases in a geometrical progression when the heights are in an arithmetical progression. If we ascend or descend $2\frac{1}{2}$, 5, or 30 miles, we find our atmosphere 10, 100, or a billion times more rarefied or more dense.

This law, although modified by the unequal temperatures of the different layers of the photosphere, and the unknown chemical nature of the substances of which it is composed, must also hold good in some measure for the sun. As, however, the mean temperature of the solar atmosphere must considerably exceed that of our atmosphere, the density of the former will not vary so rapidly with the height as the latter does. If we assume this increase and decrease on the sun to be 10 times slower than it is on our earth, it follows that at the heights of 25, 50, and 300 miles, a rarefaction of 10, 100, and a billion times respectively would be observed. The solar atmosphere, therefore, does not attain a height of 400 geographical miles, or it cannot be as much as $\frac{1}{240}$th of the sun's radius. For if we take the density of the lowest strata of the sun's atmosphere to be 1000 times greater that that of our own near the level of the sea, a density greater than that of water, and necessarily too high, then at a height of 400 miles this atmosphere would be 10 billion times less dense than the earth's atmosphere; that is to say, to human comprehension it has ceased to exist.

This discussion shows that the solar atmosphere, in comparison with the body of the sun, has only an insignificant height; at the same time it may be remarked that on the sun's surface, in spite of the great heat, such substances as water may possibly exist in the liquid state under a pressure thousands of times greater than that of our atmosphere.

Since gases, when free from any solid particles, emit, even at very high temperatures, a pale transparent light—the so-called *lumen philosophicum*—it is probable that the intense white light of the sun has its origin in the denser parts of his surface. If such be assumed to be the case, the sun's spots and faculae seem to be the disturbances of the fiery liquid ocean, caused by most powerful meteoric processes, for which all necessary materials are present, and partly to be caused by the direct influence of streams of asteroids. The deeper and less heated

174

parts of this fiery ocean become thus exposed, and perhaps appear to us as spots, whereas the elevations form the so-called faculae.

According to the experiments made by Henry, an American physicist, the rays sent forth from the spots do not produce the same heating effect as those emitted by the brighter parts.

We have to mention one more remarkable circumstance. The spots appear to be confined to a zone which extends 30° on each side of the sun's equator. The thought naturally suggests itself that some connexion exists between those solar processes which produce the spots and faculae, the velocity of rotation of the sun, and the swarms of asteroids, and to deduce therefrom the limitation of the spots to the zone mentioned. It still remains enigmatical by what means nature contrives to bring about the uniform radiation which pertains alike to the polar and equatorial regions of the sun.

VII. The Tidal Wave

In almost every case the forces and motions on the surface of the earth may be traced back to the rays of the sun. Some processes, however, form a remarkable exception.

One of these is the tides. Beautiful, and in some respects exhaustive researches on this phenomenon have been made by Newton, Laplace, and others. The tides are caused by the attraction exercised by the sun and the moon on the moveable parts of the earth's surface, and by the axial rotation of our globe.

The alternate rising and falling of the level of the sea may be compared to the ascent and descent of a pendulum oscillating under the influence of the earth's attraction.

The continual resistance, however weak it may be, which an instrument of this nature (a physical pendulum) suffers, constantly shortens the amplitude of the oscillations which it performs; and if the pendulum be required to continue in uniform motion, it must receive a constant supply of *vis viva* corresponding to the resistance it has to overcome.

Clocks regulated by a pendulum obtain such a supply, either from a raised weight or a bent spring. The power consumed in raising the weight or in bending the spring, which power is represented by the raised weight or the bent spring, overcomes for a time the resistance, and thus secures the uniform motion of the pendulum and clock. In doing so, the weight sinks down or the spring uncoils, and therefore force must be expended in winding the clock up again, or it would stop moving.

Essentially the same holds good for the tidal wave. The moving waters rub against each other, against the shore, and against the atmosphere, and thus, meeting constantly with resistance, would soon come to rest if a *vis viva* did not exist competent to overcome these obstacles. This *vis viva* is the rotation of the earth on its axis, and the diminution and final exhaustion thereof will be a consequence of such an action.

The tidal wave causes a diminution of the velocity of the rotation of the earth.

This important conclusion can be proved in different ways.

The attraction of the sun and the moon disturbs the equilibrium of the moveable parts of the earth's surface, so as to move the waters of the sea towards the point or meridian above and below which the moon culminates. If the waters could move without resistance, the elevated parts of the tidal wave would exactly coincide with the moon's meridian, and under such conditions no consumption of *vis viva* could take place. In reality, however, the moving waters experience resistance, in consequence of which the flow of the tidal wave is delayed, and high water occurs in the open sea on the average about $2\frac{1}{2}$ hours after the transit of the moon through the meridian of the place.

The waters of the ocean move from west and east towards the meridian of the moon, and the more elevated wave is, for the reason above stated, always to the east of the moon's meridian; hence the sea must press and flow more powerfully from east to west than from west to east. The ebb and flow of the tidal wave therefore consists not only in an alternate rising and falling of the waters, but also in a slow progressive motion from east to west. The tidal wave produces a general western current in the ocean.

176

This current is opposite in direction to the earth's rotation, and therefore its friction against and collision with the bed and shores of the ocean must offer everywhere resistance to the axial rotation of the earth, and diminish the *vis viva* of its motion. The earth here plays the part of a fly-wheel. The moveable parts of its surface adhere, so to speak, to the relatively fixed moon, and are dragged in a direction opposite to that of the earth's rotation, in consequence of which, action takes place between the solid and liquid parts of this flywheel, resistance is overcome, and the given rotatory effect diminished.

Water-mills have been turned by the action of the tides; the effects produced by such an arrangement are distinguished in a remarkable manner from those of a mill turned by a mountain-stream. The one obtains the *vis viva* with which it works from the earth's rotation, the other from the sun's radiation.

Various causes combine to incessantly maintain, partly in an undulatory, partly in a progressive motion, the waters of the ocean. Besides the influence of the sun and the moon on the rotating earth, mention must be made of the influence of the movement of the lower strata of the atmosphere on the surface of the ocean, and of the different temperatures of the sea in various climates; the configuration of the shores and the bed of the ocean likewise exercise a manifold influence on the velocity, direction, and extent of the oceanic currents.

The motions in our atmosphere, as well as those of the ocean, presuppose the existence and consumption of *vis viva* to overcome the continual resistances, and to prevent a state of rest or equilibrium. Generally speaking, the power necessary for the production of aerial currents may be of threefold origin. Either the radiation of the sun, the heat derived from a store in the interior of the earth, or, lastly, the rotatory effect of the earth may be the source.

As far as quantity is concerned the sun is by far the most important of the above. According to Pouillet's measurements, a square metre of the earth's surface receives on the average 4.408 units of heat from the sun per minute. Since one unit of heat is equivalent to 367 Km, it follows that one square metre of the surface of our globe receives per minute an addition of *vis viva* equal to 1620 Km, or the whole of the earth's surface in the same time 825,000 billions of Km. A power of 75 Km per second is called a horsepower. According to this, the effect of the solar radiation in mechanical work on 1 square metre of the earth's surface would be equal to 0.36, and the total effect for the whole globe 180 billions of horsepowers. A not inconsiderable portion of this enormous quantity of *vis viva* is consumed in the production of atmospheric actions, in consequence of which numerous motions are set up in the earth's atmosphere.

In spite of their great variety, the atmospheric currents may be reduced to a single type. In consequence of the unequal heating of the earth in different degrees of latitude, the colder and heavier air of the polar regions passes in an under current towards the equator; whereas the heated air of the tropics ascends to the higher parts of the atmosphere, and flows from thence towards the poles. In this manner the air of each hemisphere performs a circuitous motion.

It is known that these currents are essentially modified by the motion of the earth on its axis. The polar currents, with their smaller rotatory velocity, receive a motion from east to west contrary to the earth's rotation, and the equatorial currents one from west to east in advance of the axial rotation of the earth. The former of these currents, the easterly winds, must diminish the rotatory effect of the globe, the latter, the westerly winds, must increase the same power. The final result of the action of these opposed influences is, as regards the rotation of the earth, according to well-known mechanical principles, = 0; for these currents counteract each other, and therefore cannot exert the least influence on the axial rotation of the earth. This important conclusion was proved by Laplace.

The same law holds good for every imaginable action which is caused either by the radiant heat of the sun, or by the heat which reaches the surface from the earth's interior, whether the action be in the air, in the water, or on the land. The effect of every single motion produced by these means on the rotation of the globe, is exactly compensated by the effect of another motion in an opposite direction; so that the resultant of all these motions is, as far as the axial rotation of the globe is concerned, = 0.

178

In those actions known as the tides, such compensation, however, does not take place; for the pressure or pull by which the are produced is always stronger from east to west than from west to east. The currents caused by this pull may ebb and flow in different directions, but their motion predominates in that which is apposed to the earth's rotation.

The velocity of the currents caused by the tide of the atmosphere amounts, according to Laplace's calculation, to not more than 75 millimetres in a second, or nearly a geographical mile in 24 hours; it is clear that much more powerful effects produced by the sun's heat would hide this action from observation. The influence of these air-currents, however, on the rotatory effect of the earth is, according to the laws of mechanics, exactly the same as it would be were the atmosphere undisturbed by the sun's radiant heat.

The combined motions of air and water are to be regarded from the same point of view. If we imagine the influence of the sun and that of the interior of our globe not to exist, the motion of the air and ocean from east to west is still left as an obstacle to the axial rotation of the earth.

The motion of the waters of the ocean from east to west was long ago verified by observation, and it is certain that the tides are the most effectual of the causes to which this great westerly current is to be referred.

Besides the tidal wave, the lower air-currents moving in the same direction, the trade-winds of the tropics especially, may be assigned as causes of this general movement of the waters. The westerly direction of the latter, however, is not confined to the region of easterly winds; it is met with in the region of perpetual calms, where it possesses a velocity of several miles a day; it is observed far away from the Tropics both north and south, in regions where westerly winds prevail, near the Cape of Good Hope, the Straits of Magellan, the arctic regions, etc.

A third cause for the production of a general motion of translation of the waters of the ocean is the unequal heating of the sea in different zones. According to the laws of hydrostatics, the colder water of the higher degrees of latitude is compelled to flow towards the equator,

179

and the warmer water of the tropics towards the poles, in consequence of which, similar movements are produced in the ocean to those in the atmosphere. This is the cause of the cold under current from the poles to the equator, and of the warm surface current from the equator to the poles. The waters of the latter, by virtue of the greater velocity of rotation at the equator, assume in their onward progress a direction from west to east. It is a striking proof of the preponderating influence of the tidal wave that, in spite of this, the motion of the ocean is on the whole in an opposite direction.

Theory and experience thus agree in the result that the influence of the moon on the rotating earth causes a motion of translation from east to west in both atmosphere and ocean. This motion must continually diminish the rotatory effect of the earth, for want of an opposite and compensating influence.

The continual pressure of the tidal wave against the axial rotation of the earth may also be deduced from statical laws.

The gravitation of the moon affects without exception all parts of the globe. Let the earth be divided by the plane of the meridian in which the moon happens to be into two hemispheres, one to the east, he other to the west of this meridian. It is clear that the moon, by its, attraction of the eastern hemisphere, tends to retard the motion of the earth, and by its attraction of the western hemisphere, to accelerate the same rotation.

Under certain conditions both these tendencies compensate each otther, and then the action of the moon on the earth's rotation becomes zero. This happens when both hemispheres are arranged in a certain manner symmetrically, or when no parts of the earth can change their relative position; in the latter case a sort of symmetry is produced by the rotation.

The form of the earth deviates from a perfectly symmetrical sphere on account of the three following causes: (1) flattening of the poles, (2) the mountains on the surface, and (3) the tidal wave. The first two causes do not change the velocity of the earth's axial rotation. In order to comprehend clearly the effect of the tidal wave, we shall imagine the earth to be a perfectly symmetrical sphere uniformly surrounded by water. The attraction of the sun and the moon disturbs the equilibrium of this mass, and two flat mountains of water are formed. The top of one of these is directed towards the moon, and the summit of the other is turned away from it. A straight line passing through the tops of these two mountains is called the major axis of this earth-spheroid.

In this state the earth may be imagined to be divided into three parts—a smaller sphere, and two spherical segments attached to the opposite sides of the latter, and representing the elevations of the tidal wave. The attraction of the moon on the small central sphere does not change the rotation, and we have therefore only to consider the influence of this attraction on the two tidal elevations. The upper elevation or mountain, the one nearest the moon, is attracted towards the west because its mass is principally situated to the east of the moon, and the opposite mountain, which is to the west of the moon, is attracted towards the east. The upper tidal elevation is not only more powerfully attracted because it is nearer to the moon, but also because the angle under which it is pulled aside is more favourable for lateral deflection than in the case of the opposite protuberance. The pressure from east to west of the upper elevation preponderates, therefore, over the pressure from west to east of the opposite mountain; according to calculation, these quantities stand to each other nearly as 14 to 3. From the relative position of these two tidal protuberances and the moon, or the unchangeable position of the major axis of the earth-spheroid towards the centre of gravity of the moon, a pressure results, which preponderates from east to west, and offers an obstacle to the earth's rotation.

If gravitation were to be compared with magnetic attraction, the earth might be considered to be a large magnet, one pole of which, being more powerfully attracted, would represent the upper, and the other pole the lower tidal elevation. As the upper tidal wave tends to move towards the moon, the earth would act like a galvanometer, whose needle has been deflected from the magnetic meridian, and which, while tending to return thereto, exerts a constant lateral pressure.

The foregoing discussion may suffice to demonstrate the influence of the moon on the earth's rotation. The retarding pressure of the tidal wave may quantitatively be determined in the same manner as that employed in computing the precession of the equinoxes and the nutation of the earth's axis. The varied distribution of land and water, the unequal and unknown depth of the ocean, and the as yet imperfectly ascertained mean difference between the time of the moon's culmination and that of high water in the open sea, enter, however, as elements into such a calculation, and render the desired result an uncertain quantity.

In the mean time this retarding pressure, if imagined to act at the equator, cannot be assumed to be less than 1000 millions of kilogrammes. In order to start with a definite conception, we may be allowed to use this round number as a basis for the following calculations.

The rotatory velocity of the earth at the equator is 464 metres, and the consumption of mechanical work, therefore, for the maintenance of the tides 464,000 millions of Km, or 6000 millions of horsepowers per second. The effect of the tides may consequently be estimated at $\frac{1}{30,000}$th of the effect received by the earth from the sun.

The rotatory effect which the earth at present possesses, may be calculated from its mass, volume, and velocity of rotation. The volume of the earth is 2,650,686,000 cubic miles, and its specific gravity, according to Reich, = 5.44. If, for the sake of simplicity, we assume the density of the earth to be uniform throughout its mass, we obtain from the above premises, and the known velocity of rotation, 25,840 quadrillions of Km as the rotatory effect of the earth. If, during every second in 2500 years, 464,000 millions of Km of this effect were consumed by the ebb and flow of the tidal wave, it would suffer a diminution of 36,600 trillions of Km, or about $\frac{1}{700,000}$th of its quantity.

The velocities of rotation of a sphere stand to each other in the same ratio as the square roots of the rotatory effects, when the volume of the sphere remains constant. From this it follows that, in the assumed time of 2500 years, the length of a day has increased $\frac{1}{1,400,000}$th; or if a day be taken equal to 86,400 seconds, it has lengthened $\frac{1}{16}$th of a second, if the volume of the earth has not changed. Whether this supposition be correct or not, depends on the temperature of our planet, and will be discussed in the next section.

The tides also react on the motion of the moon. The stronger attraction of the elevation nearest to, and to the east of the moon, increases with the tangential velocity of our satellite; the mean distance of the earth and the moon, and the time of revolution of the latter, are consequently augmented. The effect of this action, however, is insignificant, and, according to calculation, does not amount to more than a fraction of a second in the course of centuries.

VIII. The Earth's Interior Heat

Without doubt there was once a time when our globe had not assumed its present magnitude. According to this, by aid of this simple assumption, the origin of our planet may be reduced to the union of once separated masses.

To the mechanical combinations of masses of the second order, with masses of the second and third order, etc., the same laws as those enunciated for the sun apply. The collision of such masses must always generate an amount of heat proportional to the squares of their velocities, or to their mechanical effect.

Although we are not in a position to affirm anything certain respecting the primordial conditions under which the constituent parts of the earth existed, it is nevertheless of the greatest interest to estimate the quantities of heat generated by the collision and combination of these parts by a standard based on the simplest assumptions.

Accordingly we shall consider for the present the earth to have been formed by the union of two parts, which obtained their relative motions by their mutual attraction only. Let the whole mass of the present earth, expressed in kilogrammes, be T, and the masses of the two portions $T-x$ and x. The ratio of these two quantities may be imagined to assume various values. The two extreme cases are, when x is considered infinitely small in comparison with T, and when $x=T-x=\frac{1}{2}T$. These form the limits of all imaginable ratios of the parts $T-x$ and x, and will now be more closely examined.

Terrestrial heights are of course excluded from the following consideration. In the first place, let x, in comparison with $T-x$, be infinitely small. The final velocity with which x arrives on the surface of the large mass, after having passed through a great space in a straight line, or after previous central motion round it, is, according to the laws developed in relation to the sun in Section III, confined within the limits of 7908 and 11,183 metres. The heat generated by this process may amount to from $8685 \times x$ to $17,370 \times x$ units, according to the value of the major axis of the orbit of x. This heat, however, vanishes by its distribution through the greater mass, because x is, according to supposition, infinitely small in comparison with T.

The quantity of heat generated increases with x, and amounts in the second case, when $x = \frac{1}{2}T$, to from $6000 \times T$ to $8685 \times T$ units.

If we assume the earth to possess a very great capacity for heat, equal in fact to that of its volume of water, which when calculated for equal weights $= 0.184$, the above discussion leads to the conclusion that the difference of temperature of the constituent parts, and of the earth after their union, or, in other words, the heat generated by the collision of these parts, may range, according to their relative magnitude, from $0°$ to $32,000°$, or even to $47,000°$!

With the number of parts which thus mechanically combine, the quantity of heat developed increases. Far greater still would have been the generation of heat if the constituent parts had moved in separate orbits round the sun before their union, and had accidentally approached and met each other. For various reasons, however, this latter supposition is not very probable.

Several facts indicate that our earth was once a fiery liquid mass, which has since cooled gradually, down to a comparatively inconsiderable depth from the surface, to its present temperature. The first proof of this is the form of the earth. "The form of the earth is its history." According to the most careful measurements, the flattening at the poles is exactly such as a liquid mass rotating on its axis with the velocity of the earth would possess; from this we may conclude that the earth at the time it received its rotatory motion was in a liquid state; and, after much controversy, it may be considered as settled that this liquid condition was not that of an aqueous solution, but of a mass melted by a high temperature.

The temperature of the crust of the globe likewise furnishes proof of the existence of a store of heat in its interior. Many exact experiments and measurements show that the temperature of the earth increases with the depth to which we penetrate. In boring the artesian well at Grenelle, which is 546 metres deep, it was observed that the temperature augmented at the rate of 1° for every 30 metres. The same result was obtained by observations in the artesian well at Mondorf in Luxembourg: this well is 671 metres in depth, and its water 34° warm.

Thermal springs furnish a striking proof of the high temperature existing in the interior of the earth. Scientific men are agreed that the aqueous deposits from the atmosphere, rain, hail, dew, and snow, are the sole causes of the formation of springs. The water obeying the laws of gravity, percolates through the earth wherever it can, and reappears at the surface in places of a lower situation. When water sinks to considerable depths through vertical crevices in the rocks, it acquires the temperature of the surrounding strata, and returns as a thermal spring to the surface.

Such waters are frequently distinguished from the water of ordinary springs merely by their possessing a higher temperature. If, however, the water in its course meets with mineral or organic substances which it can dissolve and retain, it then reappears as a mineral spring. Examples of such are met with at Aachen, Carlsbad, etc.

In a far more decided manner than by the high temperature of the water of certain springs, the interior heat of our globe is made manifest by those fiery fluid masses which sometimes rise from considerable depths. The temperature of the earth's crust increases at the rate of 1° for every 30 metres we descend from the surface towards the centre. Although it is incredible that this augmentation can continue at the same rate till the centre be reached, we may nevertheless assume with certainty that it does continue to a considerable depth. Calculation based on this assumption shows that at a depth of a few miles a temperature must exist sufficiently powerful to fuse most substances. Such molten masses penetrate the cold crust of the globe in many places, and make their appearance as lava.

A distinguished scientific man has lately expressed himself on the origin of the interior heat of the earth as follows:

"No one of course can explain the final causes of things. This much, however, is clear to every thinking man, that there is just as much reason that a body, like the earth, for example, should be warm, warmer than ice or human blood, as there is that it should be cold or colder than the latter. A particular cause for this absolute heat is as little necessary as a cause for motion or rest. Change—that is to say, transition from one state of things to another—alone requires and admits of explanation."

It is evident that this reflection is not fitted to suppress the desire for an explanation of the phenomenon in question. As all matter has the tendency to assume the same temperature as that possessed by the substances by which it happens to be surrounded, and to remain in a quiescent state as soon as equilibrium has been established, we must conclude that, whenever we meet with a body warmer than its neighbours, such body must have received at a (relatively speaking) not far distant time, a certain degree of heat,—a process which certainly allows of, and requires explanation.

Newton's theory of gravitation, whilst it enables us to determine, from its present form, the earth's state of aggregation in ages past, at the same time points out to us a source of heat powerful enough to produce such a state of aggregation, powerful enough to melt worlds; it teaches us to consider the molten state of a planet as the result of the mechanical union of cosmical masses, and thus derive the radiation of the sun and the heat in the bowels of the earth from a common origin.

The rotatory effect of the earth also may be readily explained by the collision of its constituent parts; and we must accordingly subtract the *vis viva* of the axial rotation from the whole effect of the collision and mechanical combination, in order to obtain the quantity of heat generated. The rotatory effect, however, is only a small quantity in comparison with the interior heat of the earth. It amounts to about $4400 \times T$ kilogrammetres, T being the weight of the earth in kilogrammes, which is equivalent to $12 \times T$ units of heat, if we assume the density of the earth to be uniform throughout.

186

If we imagine the moon in the course of time, either in consequence of the action of a resisting medium or from some other cause, to unite herself with our earth, two principal effects are to be discerned. A result of the collision would be, that the whole mass of the moon and the cold crust of the earth would be raised some thousands of degrees in temperature, and consequently the surface of the earth would be converted into a fiery ocean. At the same time the velocity of the earth's axial rotation would be somewhat accelerated, and the position of its axis with regard to the heavens, and to its own surface, slightly altered. If the earth had been a cold body without axial rotation, the process of its combining with the moon would have imparted to it both heat and rotation.

It is probable that such processes of combination between different parts of our globe may have repeatedly happened before the earth attained its present magnitude, and that luxuriant vegetation may have at different times been buried under the fiery débris resulting from the conflict of these masses.

As long as the surface of our globe was in an incandescent state, it must have lost heat at a very rapid rate; gradually this process became slower; and although it has not yet entirely ceased, the rate of cooling must have diminished to a comparatively small magnitude.

Two phenomena are caused by the cooling of the earth, which, on account of their common origin, are intimately related. The decrease of temperature, and consequent contraction of the earth's crust, must have caused frequent disturbances and revolutions on its surface, accompanied by the ejection of molten masses and the formation of protuberances; on the other hand, according to the laws of mechanics, the velocity of rotation must have increased with the diminution of the volume of the sphere, or, in other words, the cooling of the earth must have shortened the length of the day.

As the intensity of such disturbances and the velocity of rotation are closely connected, it is clear that the youth of our planet must have been distinguished by continual violent transformations of its crust, and a perceptible acceleration of the velocity of its axial rotation; whilst in the present time the metamorphoses of its surface are much slower, and the acceleration of its axial revolution diminished to a very small amount.

If we imagine the times when the Alps, the chain of the Andes, and the Peak of Teneriffe were upheaved from the deep, and compare with such changes the earthquakes and volcanic eruptions of historic times, we perceive in these modern transformations but weak images of the analogous processes of bygone ages.

Whilst we are surrounded on every side by the monuments of violent volcanic convulsions, we possess no record of the velocity of the axial rotation of our planet in antediluvian times. It is of the greatest importance that we should have an exact knowledge of a change in this velocity, or in the length of the day during historic times. The investigation of this subject by the great Laplace forms a bright monument in the department of exact science.

These calculations are essentially conducted in the following manner: In the first place, the time between two eclipses of the sun, widely apart from each other, is as accurately as possible expressed in days, and from this the ratio of the time of the earth's rotation to the mean time of the moon's revolution determined. If, now, the observations of ancient astronomers be compared with those of our present time, the least alteration in the absolute length of a day may be detected by a change in this ratio, or in a disturbance in the lunar revolution. The most perfect agreement of ancient records on the movements of the moon and the planets, on the eclipses of the sun, etc., revealed to Laplace the remarkable fact that in the course of 25 centuries, the time in which our earth revolves on its axis has not altered $\frac{1}{500}$th part of a sexagesimal second; and the length of a day therefore may be considered to have been constant during historic times.

This result, as important as it was convenient for astronomy, was nevertheless of a nature to create some difficulties for the physicist. With apparently good reason it was concluded that, if the velocity of rotation had remained constant, the volume of the earth could have undergone no change. The earth completes one revolution on its axis in 86,400 sidereal seconds; it consequently appears, if this time has not altered during 2500 years to the extent of $\frac{1}{500}$th of a second, or $\frac{1}{43,000,000}$th part of a day, that during this long space of time the radius of the earth also cannot have altered more than this fraction of its length. The earth's radius measures 6,369,800 metres, and therefore its length ought not to have diminished more than 15 centimetres in 25 centuries.

The diminution in volume, as a result of the cooling-process, is, however, closely connected with the changes on the earth's surface. When we consider that scarcely a day passes without the occurrence of an earthquake or shock in one place or another, and that of the 300 active volcanos some are always in action, it would appear that such a lively reaction of the interior of the earth against the crust is incompatible with the constancy of its volume.

This apparent discrepancy between Cordier's theory of the connexion between the cooling of the earth and the reaction of the interior on the exterior parts, and Laplace's calculation showing the constancy of the length of the day, a calculation which is undoubtedly correct, has induced most scientific men to abandon Cordier's theory, and thus to deprive themselves of any tenable explanation of volcanic activity.

The continued cooling of the earth cannot be denied, for it takes place according to the laws of nature; in this respect the earth cannot comport itself differently from any other mass, however small it may be. In spite of the heat which it receives from the sun, the earth will have a tendency to cool so long as the temperature of its interior is higher than the mean temperature of its surface. Between the tropics the mean temperature produced by the sun is about 28°, and the sun therefore is as little able to stop the cooling-tendency of the earth as the moderate warmth of the air can prevent the cooling of a red-hot ball suspended in a room.

Many phenomena, for instance the melting of the glaciers near the bed on which they rest, show the uninterrupted emission of heat from the interior towards the exterior of the earth; and the question is, Has the earth in 25 centuries actually lost no more heat than that which is requisite to shorten a radius of more than 6 millions of metres only 15 centimetres?

In answering this question, three points enter into our calculation;

189

(1) the absolute amount of heat lost by the earth in a certain time, say one day; (2) the earth's capacity for heat; and (3) the coefficient of expansion of the mass of the earth.

As none of these quantities can be determined by direct measurements, we are obliged to content ourselves with probable estimates; these estimates will carry the more weight the less they are formed in favour of some preconceived opinion.

Considering what is known about the expansion and contraction of solids and liquids by heat and cold, we arrive at the conclusion that for a diminution of $1°$ in temperature, the linear contraction of the earth cannot well be less than $\frac{1}{100,000}$th part, a number which we all the more readily adopt because it has been used by Laplace, Arago, and others.

If we compare the capacity for heat of all solid and liquid bodies which have been examined, we find that, both as regards volume and weight, the capacity of water is the greatest. Even the gases come under this rule; hydrogen, however, forms an exception, it having the greatest capacity for heat of all bodies when compared with an equal weight of water. In order not to take the capacity for heat of the mass of the earth too small, we shall consider it to be equal to that of its volume of water, which, when calculated for equal weights, amounts to 0.184.*

If we accept Laplace's result, that the length of a day has remained constant during the last 2500 years, and conclude that the earth's radius has not diminished $1\frac{1}{2}$ decimetres in consequence of cooling,

---

* The capacity for heat, as well as the coefficient of expansion of matter, as a rule, increases at higher temperatures. As, however, these two quantities act in opposite ways in our calculations, we may be allowed to dispense with the influence which the high temperature of the interior of the earth must exercise on these numbers. Even if, in consequence of the high temperature of the interior, the earth's mass could have a capacity two or three times as great as that which it has from $0°$ to $100°$, it is to be considered, on the other hand, that the coefficient of expansion, $\frac{1}{100,000}$, only holds good for solids, and is even small for them, whilst in the case of liquids we have to assume a much greater coefficient: for mercury between $0°$ and $100°$, it is about six times as great. Especially great is the contraction and expansion of bodies when they change their state of aggregation; and this should be taken into account when considering the formation of the earth's crust.

we are obliged to assume, according to the premises stated, that the mean temperature of our planet cannot have decreased $\frac{1}{430}°$ in the same period of time.

The volume of the earth amounts to 2650 millions of cubic miles. A loss of heat sufficient to cool this mass $\frac{1}{430}°$ would be equal to the heat given off when the temperature of 6,150,000 cubic miles of water decreases 1°; hence the loss for 1 day would be equal to 6.74 cubic miles of heat.

Fourier has investigated the loss of heat sustained by the earth. Taking the observation that the temperature of the earth increases at the rate of 1° for every 30 metres as the basis of his calculations, this celebrated mathematician finds the heat which the globe loses by conduction through its crust in the space of 100 years to be capable of melting a layer of ice 3 metres in thickness and covering the whole surface of the globe; this corresponds in one day to 7.7 cubic miles of heat, and in 2500 years to a decrease of 17 centimetres in the length of the radius.

According to this, the cooling of the globe would be sufficiently great to require attention when the earth's velocity of rotation is considered.

At the same time it is clear that the method employed by Fourier can only bring to our knowledge one part of the heat which is annually lost by the earth; for simple conduction through *terra firma* is not the only way by which heat escapes from our globe.

In the first place, we may make mention of the aqueous deposits of our atmosphere, which, as far as they penetrate our earth, wash away, so to speak, a portion of the heat, and thus accelerate the cooling of the globe. The whole quantity of water which falls from the atmosphere upon the land in one day, however, cannot be assumed to be much more than half a cubic mile in volume, hence the cooling effect produced by this water may be neglected in our calculation. The heat carried off by all the thermal springs in the world is very small in comparison with the quantities which we have to consider here.

Much more important is the effect produced by active volcanos. As the heat which accompanies the molten matter to the surface is derived from the store in the interior of the earth, their action must influence considerably the diminution of the earth's heat. And we have not only to consider here actual eruptions which take place in succession or simultaneously at different parts of the earth's surface, but also volcanos in a quiescent state, which continually radiate large quantities of heat abstracted from the interior of the globe. If we compare the earth to an animal body, we may regard each volcano as a place where the epidermis has been torn off, leaving the interior exposed, and thus opening a door for the escape of heat.

Of the whole of the heat which passes away through these numerous outlets, too low an estimate must not be made. To have some basis for the estimation of this loss, we have to recollect that in 1783 Skaptar-Jokul, a volcano in Iceland, emitted sufficient lava in the space of 6 weeks to cover 60 square miles of country to an average depth of 200 metres, or, in other words, about $1\frac{1}{2}$ cubic miles of lava. The amount of heat lost by this one eruption of one volcano must, when the high temperature of the lava is considered, be estimated to be more than 1000 cubic miles of heat; and the whole loss resulting from the action of all the volcanos amounts, therefore, in all probability, to thousands of cubic miles of heat per annum. This latter number, when added to Fourier's result, produces a sum which evidently does not agree with the assumption that the volume of our earth has remained unchanged.

In the investigation of the cooling of our globe, the influence of the water of the ocean has to be taken into account. Fourier's calculations are based on the observations of the increase of the temperature of the crust of our earth, from the surface towards the centre. But two-thirds of the surface of our globe are covered with water, and we cannot assume *a priori* that this large area loses heat at the same rate as the solid parts; on the contrary, various circumstances indicate that the cooling of our globe proceeds more quickly through the waters of the ocean resting on it than from the solid parts merely in contact with the atmosphere.

In the first place, we have to remark that the bottom of the ocean is, generally speaking, nearer to the store of heat in the interior of the earth than the dry land is, and hence that the temperature increases most probably in a greater ratio from the bottom of the sea towards the interior of the globe, than it does in our observations on the land. Secondly, we have to consider that the whole bottom of the sea is covered by a layer of ice-cold water, which moves constantly from the poles to the equator, and which, in its passage over sand-banks, causes, as Humboldt aptly remarks, the low temperatures which are generally observed in shallow places. That the water near the bottom of the sea, on account of its great specific heat and its low temperature, is better fitted than the atmosphere to withdraw the heat from the earth, is a point which requires no further discussion.

We have plenty of observations which prove that the earth suffers a great loss of heat through the waters of the ocean. Many investigations have demonstrated the existence of a large expanse of sea, much visited by whalers, situated between Iceland, Greenland, Norway, and Spitzbergen, and extending from lat. 76° to 80° N, and from long. 15° E to 15° W of Greenwich, where the temperature was observed to be higher in the deeper water than near the surface—an experience which neither accords with the general rule, nor agrees with the laws of hydrostatics. Franklin observed, in lat. 77° N and long. 12° E, that the temperature of the sea near the surface was $-\frac{1}{2}°$, and at a depth of 700 fathoms $+6°$. Fisher, in lat. 80° N and long. 11° E, noticed that the surface-water had a temperature of 0°, whilst at a depth of 140 fathoms it stood at $+8°$.

As sea-water, unlike pure water, does not posses a point of greatest density at some distance above the freezing-point, and as the water in lat. 80° N is found at some depth to be warmer than water at the same depth 10° southward, we can only explain this remarkable phenomenon of an increase of temperature with an increase of depth by the existence of a source of heat at the bottom of the sea. The heat, however, which is required to warm the water at the bottom of an expanse of ocean more than 1000 square miles in extent to a sensible degree, must amount, according to the lowest estimate, to some cubic miles of heat a day.

The same phenomenon has been observed in other parts of the

world, such as the west coast of Australia, the Adriatic, the Lago Maggiore, etc. Especial mention should here be made of an observation by Horner, according to whom the lead, when hauled up from a depth varying from 80 to 100 fathoms in the mighty Gulf Stream off the coast of America, used to be hotter than boiling water.

The facts mentioned above, and some others which might be added, clearly show that the loss of heat suffered by our globe during the last 2500 years is far too great to have been without sensible effect on the velocity of the earth's rotation. The reason why, in spite of this accelerating cause, the length of a day has nevertheless remained constant since the most ancient times, must be attributed to an opposite retarding action. This consists in the attraction of the sun and moon on the liquid parts of the earth's surface, as explained in the last section.

According to the calculations of the last section, the retarding pressure of the tides against the earth's rotation would cause, during the lapse of 2500 years, a sidereal day to be lengthened to the extent of $\frac{1}{16}$th of a second; as the length of a day, however, has remained constant, the cooling effect to the earth during the same period of time must have shortened the day $\frac{1}{16}$th of a second. A diminution of the earth's radius to the amount of $4\frac{1}{2}$ metres in 2500 years, and a daily loss of 200 cubic miles of heat, correspond to this effect. Hence, in the course of the last 25 centuries, the temperature of the whole mass of the earth must have decreased $\frac{1}{14}°$.

The not inconsiderable contraction of the earth resulting from such a loss of heat, agrees with the continual transformations of the earth's surface by earthquakes and volcanic eruptions; and we agree with Cordier, the industriousobserver of volcanic processes, in considering these phenomena a necessary consequence of the continual cooling of an earth which is still in a molten state in its interior.

When our earth was in its youth, its velocity of rotation must have increased to a very sensible degree, on account of the rapid cooling of its then very hot mass. This accelerating cause gradually diminished, and as the retarding pressure of the tidal wave remains nearly constant, the latter must finally preponderate, and the velocity of rotation therefore continually decrease. Between these two states we have a period of equilibrium, a period when the influence of the cooling and that of the tidal pressure counterbalance each other; the whole life of the earth therefore may be divided into three periods— youth with increasing, middle age with uniform, and old age with decreasing velocity of rotation.

The time during which the two opposed influences on the rotation of the earth are in equilibrium can, strictly speaking, only be very short, inasmuch as in one moment the cooling, and in the next moment the pressure of the tides must prevail. In a physical sense, however, when measured by human standards, the influence of the cooling, and still more so that of the tidal wave, may for ages be considered constant, and there must consequently exist a period of many thousand years' duration during which these counteracting influences will appear to be equal. Within this period a sidereal day attains its shortest length, and the velocity of the earth's rotation its maximum—circumstances which, according to mathematical analysis, would tend to lengthen the duration of this period of the earth's existence.

The historical times of mankind are, according to Laplace's calculation, to be placed in this period. Whether we are at the present moment still near its commencement, its middle, or are approaching its conclusion, is a question which cannot be solved by our present data, and must be left to future generations.

The continual cooling of the earth cannot be without an influence on the temperature of its surface, and consequently on the climate; scientific men, led by Buffon, in fact, have advanced the supposition that the loss of heat sustained by our globe must at some time render it an unfit habitation for organic life. Such an apprehension has evidently no foundation, for the warmth of the earth's surface is even now much more dependent on the rays of the sun than on the heat which reaches us from the interior. According to Pouillet's measurements, mentioned in Section III, the earth receives 8000 cubic miles of heat a day from the sun, whereas the heat which reaches the surface from the earth's interior may be estimated at 200 cubic miles per day. The heat therefore obtained from the latter source every day is but small in comparison to the diurnal heat received from the sun.

If we imagine the solar radiation to be constant, and the heat we receive from the store in the interior of the earth to be cut off, we should have as a consequence various changes in the physical constitution of the surface of our globe. The temperature of hot springs would gradually sink down to the mean temperature of the earth's crust, volcanic eruptions would cease, earthquakes would no longer be felt, and the temperature of the water of the ocean would be sensibly altered in many places—circumstances which would doubtless affect the climate in many parts of the world. Especially it may be presumed that Western Europe, with its present favourable climate, would become colder, and thus *perhaps* the seat of the power and culture of our race transferred to the milder parts of North America.

Be this as it may, for thousands of years to come we can predict no diminution of the temperature of the surface of our globe as a consequence of the cooling of its interior mass; and, as far as historic records teach, the climates, the temperatures of thermal springs, and the intensity and frequency of volcanic eruptions are now the same as they were in the far past.

It was different in prehistoric times, when for centuries the earth's surface was heated by internal fire, when mammoths lived in the now uninhabitable polar regions, and when the tree-ferns and the tropical shell-fish whose fossil remains are now especially preserved in the coal-formation were at home in all parts of the world.

Comments on the Mechanical Equivalent of Heat

Editorial Preface

This is Mayer's fourth full-length publication on the concept of energy. It was privately printed in 1851 by the Verlag von Johann Ulrich Landherr in Heilbronn, with the German title: *Bemerkungen über das Mechanische Aequivalent der Wärme*. It was republished in *Gesammelte Schriften und Briefe von Robert Mayer*, Jacob J. Weyrauch, 2 Vols., Stuttgart, Cotta, 1893 (Vol. 1, *Die Mechanik der Wärme*).

The following translation is that of the author of this book and is based on Weyrauch's version. An earlier translation was made by J. C. Foster and appears in *The Correlation of Forces*, an anthology edited by E. L. Youmaus, D. Appleton and Co., New York, 1886, p. 316.

As in the previous articles, the interpolated editorial notes by the present translator are intended to clarify some parts of Mayer's text from the standpoint of modern ideas. A more complete critique of the paper is found in Part II.

Introduction

The discovery of the connection between heat and motion provides the science of imponderables, which has hitherto suffered numerous complications and obscurities, a much simpler formulation; therefore the popular description here presented will be welcome to the friends of a precise view of nature.

The reason why I as a practicing physician have permitted myself to participate in the development of this important matter is provided in the essay itself.

I hope that the authorities who realize the difficulties with which one has to contend in cultivating a new field will extend a forebearing judgment to the inadequacies of my works.

Heilbronn, Christmas 1850   The Author

The lofty and extensive structure of the empirical sciences rests on a small number of supporting pillars.

History teaches us that it took millennia for the investigative spirit of man to establish the foundations of science, whereafter in a comparatively short time the building itself was erected.

And yet these fundamental principles are so clear and simple that their discovery reminds one in more than one respect of Columbus's egg.

In speaking now, when we are in possession of the truth, of a method through whose application the necessary fundamental laws could have been discovered without loss of time, we do not intend to submit the strivings and contributions of our forebears to the test of our easy criticism. Rather, it is our intention merely to convey to the reader in a heuristic fashion the increase in our knowledge obtained in the most recent times.

The most important, not to say the only, rule for scientific research is to remain mindful of the fact that it is our task to *study* the phenomena before we seek for explanations or look for higher causes. Once a fact is thoroughly known from every side, it is then explained and the task of science is concluded.

This claim may be treated by some as trivial. Others may combat it on many grounds. Nevertheless, it remains clear that this fundamental rule, even up to the present time, has been too often disregarded. It also remains clear that all speculative operations of even the most brilliant minds, which instead of making sure of the facts have sought to go beyond them, have up to now borne only empty fruits.

We shall not discuss here the modern philosophy of nature (*Naturphilosophie*) further than to say that its character is already sufficiently clear from the ephemeral existence of its offspring. But even the greatest and most meritorious natural philosophers of antiquity in order to explain, for example, the properties of the lever, took refuge in the assertion that the circle is such a marvelous thing that it is no wonder if motions taking place in a circle provide in their turn the most marvelous phenomena. If Aristotle instead of straining his extraordinary powers in meditation on the fixed point and advancing line, as he calls the circle, had investigated the numerical relations existing between the length of the lever arm and the pressure exerted, he would have laid the foundation of an important part of human knowledge.

Such errors, committed as they were in line with the spirit of those times, even by a man whose many positive services constitute his everlasting memorial, may serve to show us the opposite road which leads us surely to the goal. But if it is true that even with the use of the most correct method of investigation, nothing can be achieved without toil and industry, the reason is to be found in that divine order of the world according to which man is created for work. But certain it is that immeasurably more means and more toil have already been sacrificed to error than were needed for the discovery of truth.

199

The rule which must be followed in order to lay the foundations of natural science in the shortest possible time can be stated in few words. The phenomena nearest at hand and occurring most frequently must be subjected to the most searching examination by the senses, and this is to be continued until estimates of orders of magnitudes, expressible in numbers, have been obtained.

These numbers are the sought-for foundations of a real natural science.

Among all natural processes the free fall of a weight is the most frequently observed and the simplest and at the same time—think of Newton's apple—the most important. When one analyzes this phenomenon by the method just set forth, one soon becomes aware that the weight strikes the ground the more forcefully the higher the place from which it is dropped; the problem to be solved consists in finding the numerical relations connecting the height of fall, the time of fall and the final velocity, and to express them in terms of definite numbers.

In carrying out the experimental investigation of free fall one has to contend with various difficulties, but these can be overcome; one then reaches the conclusions that a drop from rest of about 15 feet occurs in 1 second and a final velocity of about 30 feet per second occurs in 1 second. [Mayer uses 30 feet per second per second for g here. This would be about 32 feet per second per second in ordinary English units. [In his next paragraph Mayer discusses the rise of a liquid in a tube by suction and points out the difficulty of continuing this process above a given length of tube, i.e., the barometric height, of about 28 zoll or German inches, say 30 inches, of mercury. Once one gets this number one has got something important about the phenomenon—Ed. note.]

We have learned that the pressure exerted by a liquid is proportional to the height of the liquid column and the density of the liquid. In this way we have determined the [average] density of the atmosphere and through this investigation have been led to carry the measuring instrument, the barometer, up above the surface of the earth and to express in numbers the effect which height above sea level has on the barometer reading. Through work of this kind we are led to the question whether the law of free fall, which we have established near the surface of the earth, may not suffer an alteration at greater distances from the surface. And if, as we had every right to expect, we find this is the case, we are led to ask further in what way the numbers arrived at in the earlier experiments must be modified at the greater distance from the surface of the earth.

Here we have encountered a problem whose solution involves great difficulty. For here we obviously have to deal with places on which man has never set foot in order to make observations and measurements. History teaches us, however, that the same man who raised the question was also in a position to answer it. He really could not do this without being equipped with a rich store of astronomical information. How do we proceed to get this?

Without doubt astronomy, even in its fundamental aspects, is the most difficult of all the sciences. Here we have to do with objects and spaces which forbid any thought of an experiment. The diverse motions of countless heavenly bodies are of such a complicated character that knowledge of the stars in its marvelous unfolding must be considered as the greatest triumph which the human spirit here on earth has been privileged to achieve.

Following the general rule that mankind has to proceed step by step from the simpler to the more complex, one would have expected that astronomy would have obtained its full development later than other branches of human knowledge. It is well known, however, that the facts of the case are just the opposite of this. For it was precisely in astronomy and only in this science that the most primitive peoples gained really accurate knowledge. It may indeed be safely maintained that in antiquity astronomy reached the maximum state of completeness possible in the light of the comparative failure of all the contemporary supporting sciences.

This early development of astronomy, which had really to precede the other branches of science because it alone could provide the materials necessary for the measurement of time, becomes clear when we examine all the different races of man; it is indeed in the nature of things well founded in the human spirit. It provides noteworthy evidence of the fact that a correct method is the necessary condition for successful scientific investigation.

The reason for this phenomenon, however, lies in the fact that the need for accurate time reckoning for social life made necessary the making of astronomical observations, whose results found their expression in definite *numbers*. There was a need to determine the time taken by the sun to complete its journey through the heaven of fixed stars and for the moon to go through its phases, etc. In order to meet this need it was not sufficient merely to take the book of nature in hand and treat it after the fashion of commentators and critics.

"With talk alone nothing could be created here."

(*Mit eitler Rede wird hier nichts geschafft*)

It was *numbers* which man sought for and *numbers* which were found. The spirit of research was pushed into the right path by the overwhelming force of circumstances and thereby led at once from success to success. After the needed knowledge of the paths and the distances of the closest heavenly bodies had been obtained by long continued and fortunate observation, and accurate information had been obtained about the shape and size of the earth, we have reached the state where we can handle the question what numerical influence increasing distance from the earth exerts on the law of falling bodies. We then arrive at the important result that at a height above the earth's surface equal to the radius of the earth the final velocity at the end of the first second from rest is four times smaller than at the surface of the earth.

In the continuation of our study let us return to our immediate surroundings. From the earliest times the phenomenon of combustion must have attracted the attention of people to a very high degree. In order to explain this the ancients, in accordance with their philosophical method, had to introduce an element of fire (always striving to rise), which in combination with (but actually in opposition to) air, water and earth was a part of the constitution of all things. The necessary consequence of this theory, developed by the ancients with great ingenuity, was that they remained in complete ignorance of all the relevant phenomena and everything connected therewith.

Here also it is determinations of magnitude, numbers alone, which provide us with the Ariadne thread. If we want to find out what goes on in the phenomenon of burning, we must weigh the material before and after combustion. We then find that in every combustion process different and previously separated materials combine with each other in definite weight relations and that the total weight of materials before and after combustion remains the same. We learn to recognize the various portions of matter in their separate and combined states, we learn how to transform these substances from one state to another. We find out, for example, that water is composed of two gases which combine in the ratio $1:8$. Thereby the gateway into analytical chemistry is opened to us, and stoichiometry falls into our lap like ripe fruit.

In the further course of our investigation we have learned that in all chemical processes, combinations as well as decompositions, temperature changes take place. These under varying circumstances show all gradations from the greatest to the smallest. We have been able to measure the heat developed and express it in heat units and so have determined the laws of chemical heat evolution. It has been known for a long time, however, that in a certain number of cases, heat is produced where no chemical process takes place, for example, in every case of friction, of the collision of inelastic bodies and in the compression of gases.

What then takes place in heat development of the latter sort?

History teaches that here again the ingenious hypotheses of the existence and nature of a special "heat substance" have not been able to solve this problem. Such theories have assumed a new static, non-oscillating "heat aether" as well as "heat atoms", which can play a role in the spaces separating the constituent material atoms of substances. But such theories have been of no avail, and yet heat is as wonderfully simple in its nature as is the law of the lever, over which the founder of the peripatetic philosophy beat his head against the wall in vain. [Here Mayer is less than just to Aristotle and is not sufficiently acquainted with ancient Greek science—Ed. note.]

After the foregoing the reader cannot remain in doubt what has to happen here. Again the measurement of magnitudes must be undertaken. Numbers must be found.

If we proceed in this direction and increase the quantity of heat developed through mechanical means as well as the work used up in this process and then compare these two quantities we find at once that they stand in the most simple relation to each other, an exact and unchangeable relation, and that the same relation will still hold when conversely work is produced with the help of heat.

To express these facts in succinct fashion, we say that heat and motion can be transformed into each other.

We must not stop here, however, We must know how much work is necessary to produce a given amount of heat and conversely. In other words, the law of the invariable relationship between heat and work must also be expressed in numerical form.

If through measurement we consult our experience we find that the heating of a given amount of water through 1 degree on the Celsius scale corresponds to the raising of a like weight about 1200 feet off the ground. [Taking into account the fact that the German foot is somewhat larger than the English foot, this corresponds to 3.9 joules per calorie, somewhat smaller than Joule's ultimate experimental value of 4.2 joules per calorie—Ed. note.] *This number is the mechanical equivalent of heat.*

The production of heat through friction and other mechanical processes is a fundamental fact of such universal character that its scientific establishment is worthy of note aside from any practical value of its application; therefore a historical review of matters connected therewith is not out of place here.

In the summer of 1840 I made the observation, on taking blood from newly arrived Europeans in Java, that almost without exception the blood taken from the arm veins was of a surprisingly bright red color.

This phenomenon riveted my close attention. Proceeding on the basis of Lavoisier's theory in accordance with which animal heat is the result of a combustion process, I considered the double change in color which the blood suffers in its passage through the capillaries in the small and large circulatory processes as a visible sign of an oxidation taking place in the blood. In order to maintain a uniform temperature in the human body the heat production must necessarily stand in a definite quantitative relation with the heat loss, and must also have a definite relation to the temperature of the surrounding medium. Accordingly the heat production and the oxidation process as well as the color difference between the two kinds of blood will be smaller on the whole in the tropical zone than in colder regions.

According to this theory and considering previously known physiological facts relating thereto, we have to consider the blood as a slowly burning fermenting liquid, whose principal purpose—the maintenance of a process of combustion—is attained without having the blood components themselves (except for decomposition products) leave the vascular cavities and engage in a material exchange with the organs of the body. This means in other words: the assimilated food stuff is for the most part burned (with the production of a physical effect) in the vascular cavities, and only a comparatively small quantity of it serves the much less important purpose of directly entering into the body organs and providing for the growth and replacement of solid parts that are used up.

If now it follows from this that in the organism as a whole there must be a balance between intake and outgo or between production and consumption, it is obviously a principal task of the physiologist to learn as accurately as possible the budget of his objects of investigation. The consumption consists in the burned material, the production is the development of heat. The latter takes place in two ways: the animal body in part develops heat inside itself and in turn disposes of it to its immediate surroundings, and in part, because of the capacity of its motional apparatus, possesses the ability to produce heat by mechanical action, through friction and the like. It is now necessary to know:

Whether it is the directly developed heat alone which is to be brought into the calculation of the combustion processes or rather the sum of the quantities of heat developed both directly and indirectly.

This is a crucial question in the foundations of science. In default

205

of its certain resolution a sound development of the doctrine in question is impossible. For what it means to neglect fundamental measurements has already been illustrated above. No human wit is able to replace what Nature herself provides.

The physiological theory of combustion is based on the fundamental principle that the quantity of heat which originates from the combustion of a given amount of matter is an invariant, that is, is a quantity independent of the circumstances accompanying the combustion. From this it follows that the chemical reaction of the combustible matter suffers no change in quantity through the vital processes, which further means that the living organism with all its wonderful properties is not able to produce heat out of nothing.

If we hold fast to this physiological axiom, the answer to the question posed above is already given. For if we do not give to the organism the capability to create heat, it cannot be assumed that the total quantity of heat produced by it can be greater than the yield of the chemical reaction which has taken place. Nothing remains, therefore, for the theory of combustion, if it is not to be untrue to itself, but to assume that the total heat produced by the organism in part directly and in part through mechanical action corresponds quantitatively or is equal to the yield of the combustion reaction.

From this, however, follows with the same definiteness the result that *the mechanical heat produced by the living body must stand in a quantitatively invariant relation with the work performed*. For if by differing construction of the arrangements for the production of heat *different* quantities of heat could be gained through the same abovementioned work and by the same organic combustion process, then in one and the same consumption of matter, the heat produced would be now less and now more, which contradicts the fundamental hypothesis. We note further that no qualitative difference has been found to exist between the mechanical production by animal bodies and inorganic sources of work.

It therefore follows that an invariant numerical relation exists between heat and work. This is a postulate of the physiological combustion theory.

In so far as I adhered to the direction laid down, I had necessarily to direct my attention to the physical connection between motion and heat, whereupon the existence of the mechanical equivalent of heat could not remain hidden from me. Even if I were to owe this discovery to chance, it is still my property and I do not hesitate to maintain my right to priority in discovery.

In order to insure my discovery against any eventualities, I incorporated the essential features in a short paper which I sent in the spring of 1842 to Liebig, with the request that he publish it in the *Annalen der Chemie and Phärmacie*, where it can be found in vol. 42, p. 233 under the title "Bemerkungen über die Kräfte der unbelebten Natur" (Observations on the forces of inorganic nature).

It was a favorable circumstance for me that through the well-wishing reception of that man gifted with deep insight, this unpretentious work found a place in one of the leading scientific journals. I take this opportunity publicly to thank this great scientist and express my admiration of him.

At about the same time Liebig himself had also called attention to the relation existing between heat and motion, albeit in more general terms, though quite unambiguously. He expressed it in this way: the mechanical heat produced by a steam engine must be set equal to the combustion effect, and there is no way in which the latter can be increased by having it produce mechanical action and allowing this further to be turned into heat.

From this as well as from similar statements by other scientists we may conclude that contemporary science had begun to strike out in a direction such that the existence of the mechanical equivalent of heat could no longer remain concealed.

In the above-mentioned paper the law of nature relating to the mechanical equivalent is based on a fundamental idea of the human mind. The principle that a quantity which cannot arise from nothing cannot be reduced to nothing is so clear and simple that nothing fundamental can be urged against it any more than against the axioms of geometry. We ought to accept it as true so long as no unchallenged fact has shown the contrary.

It is indeed an experimental law that both motion and heat originate at the expense of a measurable object. In countless cases motion ceases without anything else but heat making its appearance. The axiom just mentioned now demands that the disappearing motion becomes heat or in other words these two objects stand in an invariant quantitative relation with respect to each other. The test of the principle by experiment, the establishment of it in all individual cases, the proof of the existence of a complete harmony between the laws of thought and the objective world is at once the most interesting if not indeed the most all-embracing task one can find. What I have been able to contribute in this respect with rather weak resources and without support and encouragment from the outside is really little—but *ultra posse nemo obligatus.*

On the genetic connection between heat and moving force I have made the following statement in another place [page 6 of the Ostwald Klassiker edition of Mayer's 1842 paper]:

"If it has now been established that no other effect can be found for disappearing motion in many cases (*exceptio confirmat regulam*) than heat and for the heat produced no other cause than the motion, we draw the conclusion that heat arises from motion and prefer this to the assumption that there is a cause without an effect and an effect without a cause. So the chemist instead of letting hydrogen and oxygen disappear without raising the question what becomes of them and instead of letting the resultant water arise without any attempt at explanation, postulates a connection between hydrogen and oxygen on the one hand and water on the other."

From here to the goal takes only one more step. Further in the same paper [page 8 of the paper just mentioned above] we read:

"For the solution of the equations connecting the force of fall (*fall kraft*), that is, the elevation of a weight, and motion, the distance of fall for a given time, e.g., the first second, must be determined experimentally. In similar fashion the solution of the equations between "fall-force" and motion on the one hand and heat on the other needs the answer to the question: how great is the quantity of heat that corresponds to a given amount of fall-force or motion. For example, we must find how high a given weight must be raised above the surface of the earth in order that its "fall-force" may be equivalent to the heating of the same mass of water from 0 °C to 1 °C. That such a relation really exists can be treated as a resumé of the foregoing considerations.

"By application of the principle set forth to the heat and volume relations of gases we find the fall of a column of mercury compressing a gas which is equal to that due to the heat associated with the compression, and from this it emerges (taking the ratio of the specific heat capacities of air in the atmosphere at constant pressure and constant volume respectively as 1.421) that the fall of a given mass from a height of about 365 meters corresponds to the heating of the same mass of water from 0 °C to 1 °C."

It is clear that the word "equivalent" is used here in a quite different sense than in chemistry. An example will make clear the difference most emphatically. When a certain quantity of potassium hydroxide is neutralized with sulphuric acid on the one hand and with nitric acid on the other hand, we call the numbers expressing the relation in which the combining weights of these three substances stand to each other their chemical equivalents. But this terminology does not at all imply any *equality* of the substances or any transformation of material.

The special significance which the word "equivalent" has in chemistry depends undoubtedly on the fact that the chemist is granted the sight to determine quantitatively the masses of the objects of his investigation in terms of an absolute reference mass. Let us assume, however, that we could measure the one substance, water, for example, only by its weight and the other, say a gas like the water-forming mixture of oxygen and hydrogen, only by its volume. Suppose we then decided to take the mass unit as 1 pound and the volume unit as 1 cubic foot; then we should have to find out how many cubic feet of oxy-hydrogen gas can be obtained from 1 pound of water and conversely, and this number we could appropriately call the "oxy-hydrogen gas equivalent" of water.

In the latter sense, according to the laws of mechanics, the raised weight can be called the "equivalent" of the quantity of motion which is gained by the fall of the weight. In order now to reduce these two objects the raised and the moving weight (which permit no common measure) to each other, we need to introduce the number g (acceleration of gravity). It is possible to include this number in one and the same category of concepts as the mechanical equivalent of heat.

In the essay which we have been just discussing the way was opened to introduce a scientifically viable concept of force, and the importance of this circumstance prompts me to return to its consideration here.

In the higher mechanics the word "force" (*Kraft*) is used in two different senses.

1. In the first meaning force is a push or pull, or every attempt by an inert body to change its state of rest or motion. This attempt is considered for itself alone and not in terms of any consequences. The words "push force", "pull force", or simply "force" are used to distinguish this first meaning from the second meaning. In this context it is sometimes known as "dead" force.

2. In another sense force means the product of push or pull by the distance of action or the product of the mass and the square of the velocity, either by itself or one-half of it. It is thus necessary for the production of real motion that the mass in question under the influence of a push shall suffer a displacement in the direction of the push, and the product of the push and this displacement is also called "force"; but to distinguish it from the push force it is called "living force" or "motional force". [This use of the word force later was changed to apply to kinetic energy—Ed. note.]

The higher mechanics as an essentially analytical science has nothing to do with the general concept of force. In order to find the latter one must proceed in accordance with the usual rule and collect the properties associated with the different kinds of force. The definition one obtains in this way, as is well known, is: "Force" (*Kraft*) is:

"Everything which brings about motion, or tries to bring about motion, or alters motion or tries to alter motion."

But this definition is a kind of useless, diffuse and bombastic one, since we could leave out everything after the word "everything" without really changing the meaning.

This error in the attempted definition is conditioned by the nature of the problem, which really demands something impossible. Mere push (*Druck*) (dead force) and the product of force and displacement (living force) are really non-comparable things, at any rate too much so to be united in one general definition. In dynamics push or attraction is something like affinity in chemistry—an abstraction. On the other hand, the living force (*vis viva*) is like matter, something concrete. These two kinds of force (*Kraft*), though they seem to lie close together in the realm of ideas, in reality are so far apart that the space that embraces them would take in the whole world.

A way out of the difficulty may be imagined in many ways. Just as one can speak of an absolute weight and a specific weight without having any one tempted to try to make a general concept out of these different ideas, so the word "force" can be used in two or more meanings. [This sounds too much like Herbert Spencer—Ed. note.] This actually happens in the higher dynamics and hence in this science there is no problem or question of a uniform general definition of the word "force".

There has been no lack of proposals to carry through the concepts of dead and living force in separate fashion in the rest of natural science. But this has not worked. For if it is true in general that expressions with double meaning can never really contribute distinctness to discourse, their use in cases in which exchange may take place is wholly unsuitable. It is true that the mathematician does not encounter particular danger in his calculations by interchanging the factors in a given product. But in other branches of science this sort of thing can cause a complete confusion of ideas. When possible such an error must be stopped at its source, for once the word "force" is used with a double meaning it becomes the labor of Sisiphus to carry through in all details the disentanglement of the confusion that results. In order to reach our goal, we must therefore decide to give up the two meanings of the word "force" as above set forth and either to discard the concept entirely or stick to only one of the meanings cited.

It was in this sense that Newton carried through the concept of force. In the solution of his problem he broke up the product of the attraction and the displacement into two factors and called the first "force".

On the other hand, we may observe that such a subdivision of the product in question into two factors cannot always be carried out. Let us take, for example, the very simple case in which a mass M originally at rest acquires a final, uniform motion with velocity c. From M and c we can indeed draw a conclusion about the product of the Newtonian force and the displacement but not about the force itself. [What Mayer seems to mean is that the gain in kinetic energy is equal to the space integral of the force, and this does not permit us unambiguously to determine the force at each point in the path— Ed. note.]

From this the need has indeed arisen to treat this product as a whole and give it a name. People have given even this quantity the name "force" and in this sense the terms "living force of motion", "moving force", "work force", "horse force", "muscle force" have at various times entered into the scientific literature.

As happy as this choice of terminology may be considered in some respects, nevertheless it seems unfortunate that a name already in definite use should be applied to a new concept without having it removed from the old one; and this unfortunate lapse in usage has led to the opening of a Pandora's box from which a Babylonian language confusion has sprung out. [Does he here mean to refer to the Tower of Babel?—Ed. note.] Under the prevailing conditions there seems nothing left except to withdraw the name "force" from either the "dead" force of Newton or the Leibnizian "living" force (*vis viva*). In either case we come into conflict with common usage.

If, however, we have once come to the decision to introduce into science a logical terminology even at the cost of getting rid of one made convenient by custom, the choice between (1) and (2) cannot long remain in doubt.

To consider an elementary case we suppose a mass originally at rest is set in motion; this happens by virtue of the fact that it suffers a certain push or pull and under the influence of this is displaced a certain distance. Now, however, in general not only the velocity gained but the push force itself will be different at different points in the path; hence in order to find the actual motion, i.e., the effect of multiplying the force by the distance for each element of path and summing the whole, higher mathematics is necessary. [Mayer means the integral calculus—Ed. note.]

From this it follows that the Newtonian force concept (save in the case of statics, where the displacement becomes zero) is suitable only for the higher mechanics. Hence it scarcely seems appropriate to choose the concept of force in such a way that it is precisely in the elementary problems of motion to which the concept should readily apply it is not really usable.

It is, however, absurd to try to justify the use of a Newtonian force concept, like gravitation, in elementary mechanics by leaving aside the most important feature of this concept, namely its dependence on distance, and make this inexact Galilean gravity, which under certain circumstances is actually incorrect, into a force. Such an ideal third "force" seems to float before the eyes of the majority of those who write on scientific subjects as the fundamental prototype of a "natural" force.

Magnitude determinations which have only a conditional and approximate validity should not be used in the setting up of *definitions*. In practical calculations it is allowable to set an angle in radians which is sufficiently small compared with unity equal to the sine or tangent of the angle, but if one were to make this the basis of a precise concept, one would be laying the foundation for future error.

The Newtonian concept of force, as incorporated in elementary science in the customary fashion, is really no better than the concept of a rectilinear curve. The Newtonian force, or specifically the force of gravity per unit mass g, is given by the derivative of the velocity with respect to the time, that is, $g = dc/dt$ [Here c is used to denote the velocity of a particle—Ed. note.] This expression is exact, but demands for its understanding and its handling the higher mathematics [calculus—Ed. note.] However, if we are dealing with fall near the surface of the earth in which the distance of fall is a very small fraction of the earth's radius, the above formula can be approximated accurately by the simpler expression $g = c/t$. [This of course assumes that the acceleration or force per gram is constant and that c is the velocity gained after time t from rest—Ed. note.] But this formula is *not* mathematically exact as long as the distance of fall exceeds a definitely calculable value. Because of such an equation which is incorrect in principle the receptive youth has implanted in him the erroneous concept that gravity is a force producing uniform acceleration and acting proportionally to time, with other questionable notions.

It certainly would be very serviceable if the authors of textbooks of physics would correct this unfortunate situation and would lead up to their definitions through completely exact concepts and quantities. For elementary physics in its present state is not a very solid science but is only a half-baked discipline whose fundamental concepts and theorems one must try to forget as soon as possible when entering into the study of the higher branches of science.

If one has once convinced himself through unbiased tests that the force idea denoted by (1) above has nothing in its favor (and much against) except tradition, the step to take is self-evident; one must endeavor to associate the origin of every motion with an *expenditure* of force. According to this view force is something that is expended in the production of motion, and this expenditure is, as the cause of the motion, equal to the effect, which is the motion itself.

This definition not only corresponds completely with the facts but agrees as closely as possible with the existing definition in that, as I shall show, it becomes equivalent to the force concept in the higher mechanics introduced as (2) above.

If a mass M originally at rest under the influence of a push p [evidently Mayer treats this as constant—Ed. note] is moved a distance s in the direction of the push and acquires a velocity c then $ps = Mc^2/2$. [Mayer originally wrote $ps = Mc^2$, but this was corrected in a bracket in the Weyrauch text—Ed. note.] Since now in the production of any motion a push (or a pull) and a displacement are involved, it follows that a motion can never arise save at the expense of the product of such factors. This product $ps = Mc^2/2$ I call in brief a force.

214

The connection between consumption and production—or, if one prefers, the creation of the force through its effect—is illustrated in simplest fashion in the phenomenon of gravitation. It is the necessary concomitant of every motion of a falling body that the centers of mass of the two masses involved, i.e., the earth and the falling particle, should approach each other. The approach finds its natural limit in the coming together of the masses. Hence the production of the falling motion is connected with the consumption or creation of the given distance of fall (whichever way one wants to look at it) and therefore with the product of the distance of fall and the attraction. The falling of a weight to the earth is a process of mechanical combination. When the weight has finished falling the production of motion ceases, just as in the phenomenon of combustion the ability to produce heat comes to an end when the chemical reaction involved in the combination ceases. The weight lying on the surface of the earth is, like the carbon dioxide formed in combustion, none other than a *caput mortuum*. The affinity, mechanical as well as chemical, continues to exist after the combination and provides a certain resistance to the reduction. The capacity for work, however, is at an end when no more fall distance is available.

Where the attraction is vanishingly small or zero then space is no longer a real sphere of activity, and it follows from the decrease of gravity with distance that the sphere of fall also has a limit in the centrifugal direction, and that the cause of motion or the force under all circumstances has a finite value conditioned by its effect.

This fundamental physical truth can be shown most clearly by a special case involving actual numbers. If a weight of 1 pound is raised 1 foot above the earth's surface, the disposable force is 1 foot pound. If the height is n feet, then if n is not too great a number the force is n foot pounds. But if n is a very great number approaching infinity the force is by no means n foot pounds. According to Newton's law of gravitation the force will at most be r foot pounds where r is the radius of the earth in feet. [One must work out the integral of the work due to the gravitational force here to see what Mayer is getting at—Ed. note.] No matter how large the distance of fall and the time of fall may

215

be, a weight falling toward the earth cannot attain a final velocity in excess of 34,450 Paris feet per second. If, on the other hand, the earth with same volume were four times as great in mass, the force would be fourfold and the final velocity would be 68,900 Paris feet per second.

Fundamental facts of this kind must be made clear through the use of good terminology. The customary nomenclature, however, does just the opposite. As a demonstration of this we may take some statements made by an esteemed natural scientist opposing my point of view.

This gentleman [Pfaff, professor in Kiel—Ed. note] says:

"If it is completely true that in nature no motion can be destroyed, or as it is commonly expressed, the magnitude of a motion once in existence remains undiminished, and when in this sense every derived cause has the character of indestructibility, it follows that to the character of a primitive cause, that is, a true physical force, there belongs the property of indestructibility. These properties could be best developed by a closer consideration of gravity, which is the most important and the most widespread natural force (primitive cause) like the world soul, which maintains the life of the great masses on whose motions the order of the cosmos depends, in undisturbed and uncreatable fashion, without their needing any provision from outside."

If through these words a material contradiction is to exist with my view, then these same words must say that the earth's attraction by reason of its uncreatability is in a position under plausible circumstances to give a weight an infinite velocity of fall. But toward such a definite conception our author himself in several places shows a certain mistrust. Thus, among other things, he says:

"If we follow the chain of causes and effects to their first beginnings, we arrive at the true forces of nature, the primitive causes, which need no others, more primitive still, to explain their activity, which demand no replenishment, which from an uncreatable basis can likewise make ever new motions and maintain them in existence and accelerate them."

He goes on further to say:

"If the moon falls every moment a certain distance toward the earth (at least in an ideal sense), what is the force which in the following moment moves it also further from the earth, in order to produce a new force of fall? It is precisely the indestructibility and uncreatability, the ability at all times and under all circumstances to bring about at least virtually the same effect without creating anything that constitutes the essence of every true force."

The appearance in the foregoing statements at decisive places of the qualifying phrases "likewise" and "at least virtually" arouses the suspicion that our author himself does not wholly trust the ability of his "natural forces" to be able to produce an uncreated quantity of motion and the indefiniteness of his assertion is particularly significant for the protean role which the force of gravity plays in scientific writings. He gives this word a most arbitrary interpretation, and tries to return to the Newtonian concept where the facts no longer permit.

If we call gravity a force and at the same time in accordance with the customary use of language combine with this expression the representation of an object producing motion we will be led to the incorrect assumption that a mechanical production—the origination of motion—could take place without the expenditure of a measurable object. This is the reason why our author cannot make up his mind either about the facts or about his own idea. If we once allow the origination of motion out of nothing, it follows that we must allow the destruction of motion. On this assumption the quantity of motion must be simply proportional to the velocity or equal to Mc and the quantity of motion "once existing" must be set equal to $+Mc - Mc = 0$. However, the scientist we are talking about in spite of his "uncreatable forces" expressly declares motion to be undisturbable. Instead of saying precisely what becomes of the motion which disappears through friction he says in one place that it remains undecided whether the effect of the force—the quantity of motion [momentum] produced—is to be measured by the first or second power of the velocity, i.e., whether this is to be considered destructible or not.

Indeed from repeated statements he appears to consider it possible to develop infinite motion from a given amount of heat. If this were so, one would not be permitted to think of a transformation of these quantities into one another and support would be won for the contact theory. [Mayer means the contact theory of the voltaic cell, which Pfaff supported—Ed. note.]

The polemic of my honored critic whom I have introduced here as representative of the contemporary point of view, and to whom I feel indebted for his careful examination of my first [published] work, appears to me to be from the start a failure in its first object of opposing my point of view, which revolves about the *one* point of an unchangeable relation between heat and motion. This object has to be to show that the quantitative relation in question is a variable one and to indicate how this comes about. Formal controversial statements without a material basis vanish into thin air. As far as the question of forces is concerned, it is not a matter of what "force" acts on a particular thing, but rather what sort of thing ought to be called a "force". Elaborate discussions on gravity are unfruitful, for gravity is and remains a derivative of the velocity with respect to the time which is directly proportional to the mass and inversely proportional to the square of the distance, and on this point any discussion has long since been discontinued. Whether it serves any useful purpose to call this quantity a "force" is another question.

Since there has been so much misunderstanding in connection with essentially new things, I shall here document more fully and distinctly my assertions that "force of gravity" is an unsatisfactory terminology.

It is an uncontrovertible truth that the coming into existence of every motion of a falling body is bound up with the corresponding expenditure of a measurable quantity. This quantity, if it is to be an object of scientific investigation—and why should it not?—must receive a name. It has seemed proper to the genius for language, this manifestation of the logical instinct of mankind, to choose for this purpose the word "force". Since, however, this expression is already used in another sense, one might be stimulated (at any rate in fundamental science) to create a new name for the as yet unnamed concept. Before we grasp at this extreme measure, which could bring us into conflict with much that exists, it is more logical to investigate whether the word "force" which corresponds in and of itself so well to the existing requirements is really in the right place where the school first placed it.

In the language of ordinary speech we understand by "force" something that produces motion, a cause of motion, if you will. If the expression "moving force" (*vis viva*) is really a pleonasm, on the other hand the concept of a non-moving force or a "dead" force is practically a contradiction. If one says, for example, that a load which presses down with its weight on the floor exerts a force on the latter, a force which, no matter how great it is, is not able to produce the least motion, such a conception and such an expression are indeed pedagogically correct. At the same time, however, they are so artificial that they become the source of countless misunderstandings.

Between gravity and the so-called force of gravity I can detect no difference and hence I consider the latter expression unscientific.

Let not the objection be raised against me that the pressure "force", the gravity "force", the cohesion "force" constitute the "higher" causes of pressure, gravity, etc. In exact science we have to do with the *phenomena* themselves, with measurable quantities. The "first cause" of things is forever unexplainable by the mind of man: it is God, with respect to whom all "higher" cause, supernatural forces and the like belong with all their consequences in the illusory "middle" region of the philosophy of nature and in the realm of mysticism.

It is a universally valid law that waste and want go hand in hand. If in the case already discussed in which this law is fully confirmed we try for a settlement and dispense with the word "force" where it is superfluous and introduce it where we need it, we thereby get over two important obstacles. At once the entrance into the science of motion no longer depends on an acquisition of the higher mathematics. Nature now presents herself to the surprised eye in her simple beauty and even the less well-endowed intellect can grasp some things which have eluded the understanding of the greatest scholars.

Force and matter are indestructible objects. This law to which the individual facts of experience lead us in the simplest fashion and which I might therefore call metaphorically the heliocentric standpoint, is an appropriate foundation for physics, chemistry, physiology and philosophy.

Among the existing isolated facts now known but as yet only empirically confirmed which are easily referred to natural law is this: electrical and magnetic attraction no more than gravity can be isolated, and the strength of these attractions, if the distance of separation remains the same, suffers no change by the insertion of different materials (non-conductors) between them. [This is a misleading statement and incorrect unless qualified more carefully—Ed. note.]

Among the matters which remain unknown up to the present time, I mention only the influence which the ebb and flow of the tides exercises in accordance with the principles of mechanics, on the rotation of the earth. That this important situation, closely connected with the above-mentioned fundamental law, should have so far escaped the attention of scientists is factual evidence against the exclusive correctness of the system now prevailing.

For the rest, it will not have escaped the attention of those who are familiar with the more recent literature that a change in scientific terminology in line with my ideas is actually taking place; time alone, however, is effective in these things.

According to the foregoing we have to call the moving "force" (*vis viva*) a force: since, however, in mechanics we have to understand by this both the product of the mass of an object and the square of its velocity as well as a quantity proportional to the product of the mass (the weight) and the distance of fall, this force naturally falls into two easily distinguishable forms, each of which deserves a special name, for which the words *motion* and *"fall-force"* appear to me to be the most appropriate.

According to this definition "motion" is always to be represented by a measurable quantity given by the product of the moving mass by one-half the square of the velocity and not by the product of the mass by the velocity.

By "fall-force" or force associated with fall we shall understand a raised weight or more generally the spatial displacement of ponderable objects. In many cases the magnitude of the fall-force is measured with sufficient accuracy by the product of the weight of the object and the height to which it is raised, and the expression "foot pound", "meter kilogram", "horsepower" [more accurately horse-force since horsepower is a unit of power—Ed. note] are conventional units of measure of this force, which are indeed currently employed in practical mechanics. In order, however, to find the exact expression for the quantities in question we have at the very least to think of two masses which are separated from each other by a definite distance and then acquire motion by approaching each other. We must then find the relation which exists between the conditions of the motion, that is, the mass magnitudes, their original separation as well as their eventual separations and the corresponding motions themselves.

It is noteworthy that this relation is the simplest that can be contemplated, for according to the Newtonian law of gravitation the quantities of motion arising are directly proportional to the masses and the displacement in the motion, but at the same time inversely proportional to the two distances from the center of mass. That is, if A and B are the two masses, c and c' the velocities attained, h and h' the two separations of the masses respectively, then we have

$$Ac^2 + Bc'^2 = \frac{AB(h - h')}{hh'}.$$

In words, the fall-force is equal to the product of the masses by the net displacement (or change in separation) divided by the product of the two distances of separation (original and final). [Mayer omits the constant of gravitation G on the right-hand side of the equation and the factor $\frac{1}{2}$ on the left—Ed. note.]

With the help of this theorem, which as we can easily see is merely a more general and convenient expression of the Newtonian gravitational law, we can develop the law for the fall of an object from a cosmic distance (e.g., to the earth or sun) and indeed handle in general all central motions, without needing to proceed from equations of the second degree.*

Now that we have learned to distinguish the two kinds of force, namely motion and fall-force, we can form the unified concept of "force", according to the well-known rule, by combining the common properties of both kinds. To this end we must examine the common properties of these objects. The most important of these rests on their mutual relation. When a given quantity of fall-force disappears, motion results, and through the expenditure of the latter, the original quantity of fall-force is again attained.

This constant proportion existing between fall-force and motion which is introduced in higher mechanics under the name of the principle of the conservation of *vis viva* [incidentally an unfortunate terminology—Ed. note] can be denoted more briefly and appropriately by the expression "transformation". For example, we can say that a planet which moves from a position far from the sun to a position nearer to the sun transforms a part of its fall-force into motion, and when it recedes from the sun transforms a part of its motion into fall-force.

The development of a definite amount of motion from a given amount of fall-force and conversely implies, in accordance with the axiom set-up previously (i.e., from nothing comes nothing), that neither the fall-force nor the motion can become zero either in whole or in part. We therefore obtain the following definition:

Forces are transformable and indestructible entities and in contradiction to matter are imponderable.

* The Newtonian formula applies to the special case in which the two separations are equal and the product of the two is the square of either. In this case the net displacement as well as the velocities become zero, and hence here when one wishes to calculate real velocities one has to employ mathematical methods which cannot be applied in elementary science. [This is a strange statement. Taken at its face value, it seems to indicate that Mayer was completely confused about the relation between the equation just presented above, which is the correct energy equation for the gravitational interaction of two particles, and the Newtonian gravitational force equation—Ed. note.]

222

Among other things one easily sees that this definition includes the fact that motion which vanishes in different mechanical processes stands in a constant ratio to the heat which is produced; motion as an indestructible entity can be transformed into heat. Accordingly, heat like motion is a force and motion like heat is an imponderable.

The relation in which forces stand to each other I have characterized by naming them different forms of one and the same entity. In this connection, however, I have expressly declared myself against the closely associated but in my opinion unwarranted and too far-reaching conclusion that heat phenomena are to be considered after all merely as motion phenomena. In my 1842 paper, I said:

"From the relation connecting fall-force and motion we are not permitted to say that the essence of fall-force *is* motion. Neither are we allowed to say this about heat. We must rather proceed in opposition to this and say that in order to become heat, motion, whether it be simple or vibrating (like light), radiant heat, etc., must cease to be motion." [Mayer evidently could not accept the molecular theory of the constitution of matter so far as its connection with the mechanical theory of heat is concerned—Ed. note.]

The relation between heat and motion, as we have seen, is connected with *quantity* and not with *quality*. To express the matter as Euclid would, there are objects which are equal to each other, but not really similar to each other. One must be careful not to leave objective ground if one does not wish to fall into self-made difficulties!

In the meantime we can be assured from what has gone before that there are no specific fluids to which the phenomena of heat, electricity and magnetism owe their existence; the immaterial nature of heat maintained by Rumford half a century ago has been confirmed by the discovery of the mechanical equivalent of heat.

The form of "force" denoted by the term "heat" is evidently not a unique one. Under this term there are subsumed entities which, though *equivalent*, are of different kinds. According to custom three principal forms are distinguished, viz. I, radiant heat, II, free specific heat, and III, latent heat.

No doubt can be raised about considering radiant heat as a motional phenomenon. Interference phenomena have recently been shown to hold for heat radiation. Whether there really exists a specific fluid aether, as some assume, whose vibrating motion manifests itself as radiant heat or whether this motion is associated with the constituent particles of different material bodies themselves, has not yet been decided.

The essence of specific heat, or what goes on in the inside of a body that has been heated, lies even more in the dark. Here not only the unsolved aether problem may play a role, but in order to come to grips with this problem we must learn more about the innermost nature of matter. But here in many respects we remain in ignorance, for in particular we really do not know whether atoms exist, i.e., whether matter is made up of such constituent parts, which do not change their form in chemical reactions.

Man is highly restricted in his attempts at scientific investigation. He is limited to only a small interval of time which stretches infinitely far both in the past and the future. He may take but few steps up and down. In his knowledge of the infinitely great as well as the infinitely small he is severely restricted. The atomic question, however, appears to lead us beyond these limits and for that reason I hold it to be impractical. An atom in itself, like a mathematical differential, cannot be the object of our investigation, although the relation in which such immeasurably small tool quantities stand to each other is representable in terms of concrete numbers. In every case, however, the concept of atom is to be taken only in a relative sense and in relation to a definite process. For example, in the formation and composition of a salt, the mass particles of the acid and the base, as is well known, can play the role of atoms themselves undergoing further decomposition.

Let us assume, which at the present time can be done with some degree of probability from the law of isomorphism, that chemical reactions really take place in terms of atoms; we then have to answer the further question whether by continued subdivision of a piece of matter we arrive finally at molecules which act as atoms with respect to heat phenomena in the sense that heat is unable to penetrate into them and that their volume does not change in the heating of the material. Since the fundamental points of departure for the answer of such necessary preliminary questions fail us, we must be contented with the statement that with or without the assumption of aether and atoms we find ourselves in a state of ignorance with respect to the nature of specific heat.

The expression "latent heat" is related to the recognized property of the indestructibility of heat. In all cases in which the thermometrically perceptible specific heat vanishes it must be assumed that this has merely withdrawn itself from our perception, that it has assumed another form and that by means of a suitable process the free heat can once more become evident in its original magnitude. This is the essential fact concerning latent heat and in so far as one holds fast to this one can reconcile all associated phenomena with the principle of the transformation and conservation of force.

According to this view the concept of latent heat is none other than that of an entity equivalent to free heat, and hence the doctrine of free and latent heat embraces nearly the whole of physics. A few examples from the whole subject may serve to show the way in which the phenomena in which heat becomes latent are to be understood from my point of view.

When heat is communicated to a gas at constant pressure the free heat of the gas is increased and at the same time a calculable quantity of heat becomes latent. In this process the gas expands and thereby a quantity of *vis viva* is produced which is proportional to the product of the pressure and the increase in volume. As soon as we know how much of the latent heat is attributable to the expansion of the gas we also know the amount of latent heat left over after the *vis viva* has been produced. Now Gay-Lussac has shown through his investigations that when a gas streams out of a container into a vacuum there is no perceptible change in its specific heat. [Actually this means no change in temperature—Ed. note.] From this we conclude that a gaseous body offers no appreciable resistance to the separation of its constituent parts and that in the decrease in density of such a gas by free expansion in which there is no development of force no heat becomes latent. Consequently we conclude that in the expansion of a gas in general the whole latent heat is equivalent to the *vis viva* produced.

From the principle of the indestructibility of heat, which no one doubts, it follows that the quantity of heat which has become latent in this way must again become free if the motion associated with the *vis viva* produces heat in any fashion. Motion is latent heat and heat is latent motion.

A special application of this general principle is the celebrated law of Dulong: the quantities of heat which are obtained by the compression of gases depend only on the consumption of force and not on the chemical constitution, the pressure and temperature of the gas. That, however, this general law has an even more general validity and that in the expansion of a gas the quantity of heat becoming latent reappears in every case when one employs the *vis viva* to produce heat, either through gas compression, friction or inelastic collisions, I say I have set forth in my 1842 essay to which reference has frequently been made. There I calculated the mechanical equivalent of heat on the basis of assumptions which cannot be contradicted.

As a confirmatory test I have measured the heat produced in the hollanders in the manufacture of paper and have compared this with the work force [energy] consumed; I found a satisfactory agreement. More recently I have succeeded in constructing a very simple heat-motion measuring device for the small-scale determination of the mechanical equivalent of heat. It is possible by means of this to provide an ocular demonstration of the correctness of the principle in question. I have reason to believe that by the use of my device the efficiency of water power plants and steam engines can easily be measured. However, it must be left to the judgment of the technologists to decide whether and to what extent my method is to be preferred to that of Prony. [Prony brake—Ed. note.]

A latency of heat also takes place in certain changes in states of aggregation of substances. It is a well-confirmed fact that solid as well as liquid bodies offer a certain resistance to the separation of their parts. Since the overcoming of mechanical resistance in general demands a consumption of *vis viva* we may suspect *a priori* that when the cohesion of a body is diminished or reduced to nothing force [energy] or heat must become latent. This agrees well with experience.

Proceeding from this point of view the French physicist Person has tried to show experimentally that the latent heat of melting of metals, concerning which he has made numerous observations, has a direct quantitative relation to the cohesion of these substances. However, at the present time such observations are afflicted with difficulties that are hard to overcome.

In similar fashion in his important work "On heat and elasticity of gases and vapors" (Mannheim, 1845) Holtzmann has discussed the latent heat of vaporization of water. Proceeding from the principle that the raising of a weight is equivalent to increase in temperature, he calculates the mechanical equivalent of heat from the latent heat associated with the expansion of a gas. He quite correctly breaks up the latent heat of the vapor into two parts. The one part (and the smaller of the two) is used to overcome the opposing atmospheric pressure. This can be readily determined with the help of the mechanical equivalent of heat. The part left over, which is now calculable, Holtzmann calls the heat needed to overcome the cohesion of water. It is the latter which is lost in the action of all steam engines. Holtzmann calculates from these premises how much more efficient high-pressure engines are than the low-pressure variety.*

If the above conception of the latent heats of fusion and vaporization is correct, it follows that in the pulverization of solid bodies a latent heat must be observed. Therefore, when such bodies change from the finely divided solid state to the liquid state they must bind a smaller amount of heat than when the transfer takes place from the undivided solid state. Several attempts on my part to settle this point have led to no conclusive results.

It is also noteworthy that certain solid bodies able to undergo allotropic change, for example, the oxides of iron, are able to develop

* The greatest efficiency is obtained from those engines in which heat is contributed to the steam during its expansion.

considerable quantities of heat in the transitions from the state of smaller to that of greater hardness. Such facts, which will undoubtedly become more numerous as time passes, agree well with the above-mentioned principle that increased cohesion is connected with force and heat consumption, and on the other hand increase in cohesion is associated with heat production.

The currently prevailing terminology which gives gravity the designation of *vis viva* and calls heat a substance [caloric] has led to the consequence that the significance of an important entity of nature, namely the displacement in free fall of an object, is pushed as far away as possible from our consciousness. At the same time heat gets a position far removed from the *vis viva* or motion-force. The scientific system then becomes a very artificial one that can be handled with assurance only by means of higher mathematical analysis.

It is doubtless owing to this unfortunate circumstance that the close and simple connection between heat and motion has remained hidden until comparatively recent times. As has already been pointed out above, in the meantime the measurement of chemical heat effects and galvanic actions as well as the researches on vital phenomena carried out in the spirit of Liebig led of necessity to the simple law of the equivalence of heat and motion.

In fact, this law and its numerical expression, the mechanical equivalent of heat, were published almost simultaneously in Germany and England.

Proceeding from the fact that the magnitude of both chemical and galvanic action depends wholly and only on the amount of material consumed, the celebrated English physicist Joule was led to the principle that motion and heat phenomena rest essentially on one and the same basis, or as he expresses it, in the same fashion as myself, heat and motion can be transformed with each other.

It cannot be denied that this great scientist (Joule) discovered independently the law of nature of which we have been speaking. But he has also made countless other important contributions to the further development of the idea. Joule has shown that if motion is developed by means of electromagnetism [electric motor] the heating effect of the driving electric current is diminished in a correspondingly constant proportion. He has further shown that in the reversal of the poles of a bar magnet a quantity of heat is developed which is proportional to the square of the magnetic field intensity, a fact which I also discovered, though later than Joule. In particular, Joule has demonstrated by means of many investigations that the heat developed under different conditions by friction always has an invariant relation to the force [mechanical energy] used up. From the latest investigation of this kind he has placed the mechanical equivalent of heat at 423.*

Joule has also made experimental investigations of the thermal behavior of elastic fluids [gases] and has thereby confirmed the results of early investigators.

The new situation soon began to attract the attention of scientists. Since, however, this was treated both in this country and abroad as an exclusively foreign discovery, I was forced to the necessity of making good my fundamental claims to priority. For though the few works published by me, which have disappeared almost without trace in the flood of publications which every day brings forth, demonstrate in their form that I do not hanker after effect, that does not in any way indicate an inclination to forfeit my documented property rights.

With the help of the mechanical equivalent of heat, problems can be solved which cannot be attacked without it. In particular we think here of the calculation of the heat produced in the collision of cosmic masses. A brief reference to this is in order here.

An example of this sort would be the following. Let us assume that a cosmic object enters the earth's atmosphere with a velocity of 4 geographical miles per second and let us suppose that it loses through the resistance to its motion as much of its *vis viva* so that its velocity at the earth's surface becomes 3 miles per second. The question is: How large is the heating effect which takes place?

By using the mechanical equivalent of heat we find through a simple

* This means that 1 calorie of heat is equivalent to 423 meter kilograms of work.

calculation that the quantity of heat in question is approximately 7 times greater than the heat of combustion of an equal mass of carbon, the latter being 6000 calories per kilogram. From this we conclude that the velocity with which the shooting stars move, and which according to astronomical observations runs from 4 to 8 miles per second, is fully capable of producing the most intense heat. We thereby gain an insight into the nature of these remarkable phenomena.*

A problem of similar kind is the following. When two cosmic masses which move in space about their common center of gravity collide due to some influence such as the resistance of the surrounding medium, it may be asked: How large is the heat effect corresponding to the collision?

Even if we do not know the elements of the orbits, that is their eccentricities, from the given masses and volumes we can still calculate maximum and minimum values of the effect that is sought. For example, we may assume that our earth is divided into two equally great spheres which have united in the manner described. Calculation shows that in every case significantly more heat is developed thereby than by the combustion of an equal weight of material in the most intense chemical process known.

It is more than probable that our earth originated in this way and that as a consequence of this process our sun seen from the distance of the fixed stars manifested at that time an extraordinary expansion of its light. What took place in our solar system millions of years ago is probably going on at the present time here and there in the universe of the fixed stars. We may be able to explain in this way the remarkable phenomena of stars like the famous new star of Tycho which occasionally shine forth with extraordinary brilliance. This phenomenon may receive its most satisfactory explanation through the collision of two previously invisible double stars.

The steady radiation from most fixed stars, including our sun, through enormous periods of time would seem to stand in contrast

* The view that the meteors under discussion owe their light to mechanical processes, whether friction or air compression, is not new. But it cannot be scientifically grounded without a knowledge of the mechanical equivalent of heat.

to such explosive light production. Does the steady radiation pheno-menon present a real exception to the natural laws which we have previously found to be confirmed by experience and explained by the creation of the cause through the effect? Or is it permitted even here in the small sum total of man's knowledge to think of an equilibrium between production and consumption and to investigate the conditions under which such can exist?

A closer examination of this situation would lead us beyond the purpose of this essay. So I close in the hope that it may please the reader to supplement what has been left unsaid here by his own meditation.

Index

GALILEI, G.   22, 76, 213
Gas, free expansion of   34, 82
Gastrocnemius   129
GAY-LUSSAC, J. L.   7, 9, 34, 53, 82
Geometer   77
Glaciers   189
Gravitation   158f, 181, 213, 221f
Gravity   69, 217f
Grist mill   89
Gulf stream   194

Heart   38f
   action in man   112, 120
   consumption of energy by   128f
   function in metabolism   132
   palpitation   134
Heat
   absorption of, by transparent bodies   164f
   as a form of energy   81
   as a substance (caloric)   30, 52f, 149, 203
   atomic theory of   53
   cubic mile of   152
   diathermic energy of   165
   due to friction   29, 71
   forms of   224
   internal, of organism   126
   kilocalorie as unit of   150
   nature of   52f, 223
   of combustion of carbon   85
   physical sources of   149ff
   produced on impact   45
   production by friction   204
   production in animals   105f
   relation to mechanical energy   85
   relation to motion   31
   transformation into motion   81f
   transformation into work   204
Heat engine   24, 37
Heliography   173
HELMHOLTZ, H.   10, 12, 15, 35, 46f, 48, 52
HENRY, J.   175
HERSCHEL, J.   148f, 152, 170f
Hibernating animals   126f

HOLTZMANN, C.   118, 227
Horsepower   36, 103f
HUMBOLDT, F. W. H. A.   193
Hydrogen
   heat capacity of   190
   heat of combustion of   94

Impenetrability   68
Incandescence   148
Indestructibility of forces   60
Innervation in muscles   141, 142f
Involuntary motion   141f
Iron in red blood cells   129
Irritability
   of muscles   40, 135ff, 137
   permanence of   137
Isomorphism, law of   224

JOULE, J. P.   9, 71, 53, 47, 228f
   paddle box experiment   30

KANT, I.   47
KELVIN, LORD (Sir William Thomson)   9, 11, 12, 46, 51f, 71
KEPLER, J.   157
Kilogram calorie   87
Kinetic energy   22, 105, 151
KOHLRAUSCH, F. W. G.   106f

LAGRANGE, J. L.   22
LAPLACE, P. S.   47, 175, 179, 188f, 195
Latent heat   53, 83, 96, 224f
   of fusion and vaporization   227
Lava   185
LAVOISIER, A.   24, 105, 107, 204
Laws of nature, universal applicability of   163
LEIBNIZ, G. W.   22, 28, 68, 70, 90
Lever   96, 199
LIEBEG, J.   7, 11, 84, 105f, 109f, 117, 124, 129, 207, 228
LITTROW, J. J.   158
Lung
   capillaries   125
   role of, in metabolism   118f